New Songs of Inspiration

Compiled by W. Elmo Mercer

BS00443
25986-0430-7

BRENTWOOD-BENSON
music publishing

© 1980 Brentwood-Benson Music Publishing, Inc. 741 Cool Springs Blvd., Franklin, TN 37067.
rights reserved. Unauthorized duplication prohibited. Distributed by PROVIDENT MUSIC DISTRIBUTION, INC.
1-800-846-7664

25-09-03

Foreword

There are multiplied thousands of beautiful gospel songs. New and old they beckon for recognition and present themselves to be published. From this wealth of inspired poetry and music we have collected the thrilling songs in this book. Some you will surely recognize as old friends and acquaintances. These will lead you down familiar paths of faith, devotion and aspiration. Others are fine young songs eagerly awaiting the opportunity to stir and warm hearts, bringing a new found joy with their rich, spiritual truths. It is our hope that you will become warm friends with them all, and that the inspiring songs in this treasured collection will become a constant source of strength and inspiration in the joys and sorrows of life.

Reprinted from the pen of John T. Benson, Jr. in Volume Four, published in 1961.

Acknowledgements

The Inspiration series has traditionally contained the great old songs and hymns of the revered writers of the past. From the rich legacy of praise and worship of these devout hearts we have chosen many of the songs for this collection.

Included are great songs by Fanny J. Crosby, Howard E. Smith, J. Edwin McConnell, George Bernard, B. B. McKinney, N. B. Vandall, P. P. Bliss, James D. Walbert, W. B. Walbert, Harry Dixon Loes, Robert Lowry, A. H. Ackley, C. C. Stafford, G. T. Speer, Will M. Ramsey, J. H. Fillmore, E. M. Bartlett, William Edie Marks, Luther G. Presley, Adger M. Pace, R. E. Winsett, Emmett S. Dean, Charles D. Tillman, J. B. Coates, Hamp Sewell, Charles Gabriel, Charles P. Jones, G. C. Morris, F. M. Lehman, George C. Stebbins, Johnson Oatman, Jr., Charles Weigle, Brantley George, James Rowe, V. O. Stamps, Charles Durham, Thomas Ramsey, A. J. Showalter, C. Austin Miles, Wm. M. Golden, J. M. Henson, Charles E. Moody, Thomas J. Laney, J. E. Thomas, Wm. S. Pitts, Albert E. Brumley, Cleavant Derricks, Alphus LeFevre, A. J. Sims, Charles H. Marsh, W. H. Doane.

Acknowledgements

From the songwriters and composers of today we have included a wide variety of new songs and special favorites. We are indebted to such writers as Ira Stanphill, Marvin P. Dalton, John R. Sweeney, John W. Peterson, W. Elmo Mercer, Ben Speer, Lois Irwin, Dottie Rambo, Gordon Jensen, Steve Adams, Jim Hill, Richard Blanchard, Phil Johnson, John Stallings, Henry Slaughter, Harold Lane, Dallas Holm, Marietta and Lanny Wolfe, Danny Lee, Mosie Lister, V. B. (Vep) Ellis, E. W. (Bill) Suggs, Ray Overholt, Elmer Cole, Squire Parsons, Jr., Dave Clark, Jack Clark, Chuck Millhuff, Charles B. Wycuff, Charles B. Feltner, Byron L. Whitworth, Joel Hemphill, Joel Hemphill, Jr., Reba Rambo, Stuart K. Hine, Milton Bourgeois, Neil Enloe, Conrad Cook, Andrae Crouch, Alfred B. Smith, David Huntsinger, J. D. Sumner, Candy Hemphill, James McFall, David Ingles, Roger L. Horne, Kenneth Morris, Clarence Williams, Ralph Carmichael, Robert S. Arnold.

Dedication

To those who have a natural love and a yearning to sing gospel songs in the church and home and also to those evangels who sing abroad the land giving inspiration and comfort to great American audiences–this book is dedicated.

Reprinted from the pen of John T. Benson, Jr. in Volume Four, published in 1961.

Rock of Ages

1

Augustus M. Toplady

Thomas Hastings

1. Rock of A - ges, cleft for me, Let me hide my - self in Thee,
2. Could my tears for - ev - er flow, Could my zeal no lan - guor know,
3. While I draw this fleet - ing breath, When my eyes shall close in death,

Let the wa - ter and the blood, From Thy wound-ed side which flowed,
These for sin can - not a - tone, Thou must save, and Thou a - lone,
When I rise to worlds un - known, And be - hold Thee on Thy throne,

Be of sin the dou - ble cure, Save from wrath and make me pure.
In my hand no price I bring, Sim - ply to Thy cross I cling.
Rock of A - ges, cleft for me, Let me hide my - self in Thee.

2 Trust and Obey

Rev. J. H. Sammis

D. B. Towner

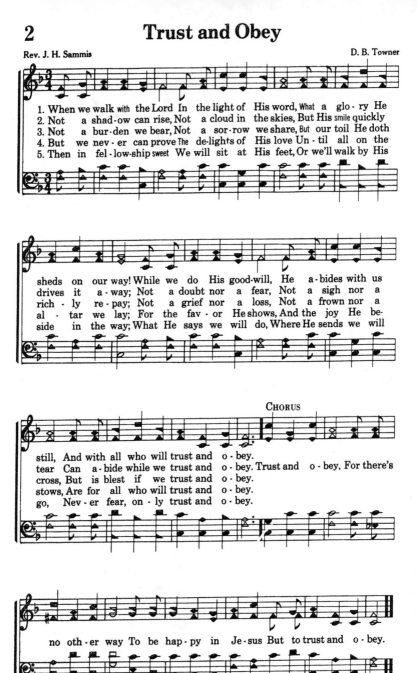

1. When we walk with the Lord In the light of His word, What a glo·ry He
2. Not a shad·ow can rise, Not a cloud in the skies, But His smile quickly
3. Not a bur·den we bear, Not a sor·row we share, But our toil He doth
4. But we nev·er can prove The de·lights of His love Un·til all on the
5. Then in fel·low·ship sweet We will sit at His feet, Or we'll walk by His

sheds on our way! While we do His good·will, He a·bides with us
drives it a·way; Not a doubt nor a fear, Not a sigh nor a
rich·ly re·pay; Not a grief nor a loss, Not a frown nor a
al·tar we lay; For the fav·or He shows, And the joy He be·
side in the way; What He says we will do, Where He sends we will

CHORUS

still, And with all who will trust and o·bey.
tear Can a·bide while we trust and o·bey.   Trust and o·bey, For there's
cross, But is blest if we trust and o·bey.
stows, Are for all who will trust and o·bey.
go, Nev·er fear, on·ly trust and o·bey.

no oth·er way To be hap·py in Je·sus But to trust and o·bey.

Lift Him Up!

3

R. R.

Reba Rambo

1. Lift Him up! Lift Him up! ___ Lift the name of Je - sus
2. Praise the Lord! Praise the Lord! ___ Praise His right - eous - ness for -
3. Show His love! Show His love! ___ Show His love to ev - 'ry -

high - er. Lift Him up, Raise His ban - ner to ___ the sky. ___
ev - er. Praise the Lord, Lift your voic - es to ___ the sky. ___
bod - y. Show His love, Let your can - dle al - ways shine. ___

___ He said, "If I be lift - ed up, I will draw all men un -
___ He said if we won't praise His name, then the rocks and stones will
___ He said that by the love we show, they will know we're His dis -

to ___ me," Lift Him up, all ye peo - ple, lift Him up! ___
cry ___ out. Praise the Lord, all ye peo - ple, praise the Lord! ___
ci - ples. Show His love, all ye peo - ple, show His love! ___

4

How Great Thou Art!

Swedish melody
Arr. by Manna Music, Inc.

Trans. by Stuart K. Hine

1. O Lord my God, when I in awe-some won - der
2. When through the woods and for - est glades I wan - der
3. And when I think that God, His Son not spar - ing,
4. When Christ shall come with shout of ac - cla - ma - tion

Con - sid - er
And hear the
Sent Him to
And take me

all the worlds Thy hands have made, ____ I see the stars, I hear the
birds sing sweet - ly in the trees, ____ When I look down from loft - y
die, I scarce can take it in— ____ That on the cross, my bur - den
home, what joy shall fill my heart! ____ Then I shall bow in hum - ble

*roll - ing thun - der, Thy pow'r through-out the un - i - verse dis - played! ____
moun - tain gran - deur And hear the brook and feel the gen - tle breeze, ____
glad - ly bear - ing, He bled and died to take a - way my sin! ____
ad - o - ra - tion And there pro - claim, my God how great Thou art! ____

CHORUS

Then sings my soul, my Sav - ior God, to Thee; ____ How great Thou

*Author's original words were "works" and "mighty."

© Copyright 1953, 1955 by MANNA MUSIC, INC., 2111 Kenmere Ave.,
Burbank, CA 91504. International copyright secured. All rights reserved.
Used by permission.

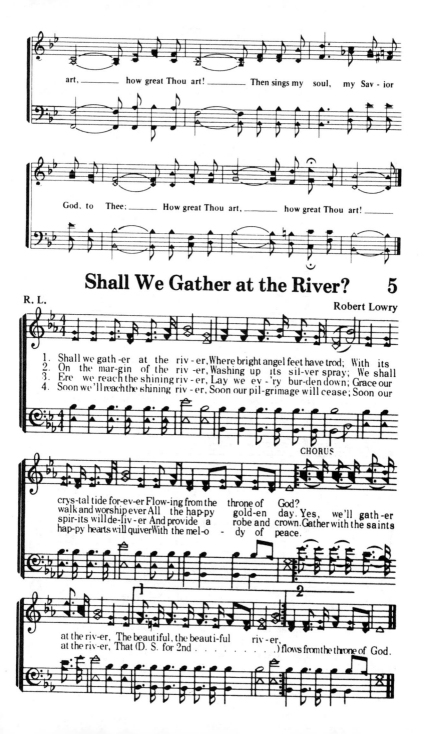

art, _____ how great Thou art! _____ Then sings my soul, my Sav - ior

God, to Thee; _____ How great Thou art, _____ how great Thou art! _____

Shall We Gather at the River?   5

R. L.

Robert Lowry

1. Shall we gath-er at the riv-er, Where bright angel feet have trod; With its
2. On the mar-gin of the riv-er, Washing up its sil-ver spray; We shall
3. Ere we reach the shining riv-er, Lay we ev-'ry bur-den down; Grace our
4. Soon we'll reach the shining riv-er, Soon our pil-grimage will cease; Soon our

CHORUS

crys-tal tide for-ev-er Flow-ing from the throne of God?
walk and worship ever All the hap-py gold-en day. Yes, we'll gath-er
spir-its will de-liv-er And provide a robe and crown. Gather with the saints
hap-py hearts will quiver With the mel-o - dy of peace.

1.
at the riv-er, The beautiful, the beauti-ful riv-er,
2.
at the riv-er, That (D. S. for 2nd . . . .) flows from the throne of God.

6 Each Step I Take

W. E. M.

W. Elmo Mercer

1. Each step I take my Sav-iour goes be-fore me, And with His lov-ing hand
2. At times I feel my faith be-gin to wa-ver, When up a-head I see
3. I trust in God, no mat-ter come what may, For life e-ter-nal

He leads the way. And with each breath I whis-per "I a-dore Thee;" Oh, what
a chas-m wide, It's then I turn and look up to my Sav-iour, I am
is in His hand, He holds the key that o-pens up the way, That will

Rit. CHORUS

joy to walk with Him each day. . . . . .
strong when He is by my side. . . . . . . Each step I take I know that He will
lead me to the promised land. . . . .

guide me; To high-er ground He ev-er leads me on. Un-til some day the last

Rit.

step will be tak-en, Each step I take just leads me clos-er home.

Jesus Is the Sweetest Name I Know 7

L. L.

Lela Long

1. There have been names that I have loved to hear, But nev - er has there
2. There is no name in earth or Heav'n a - bove, That we should give such
3. And some - day I shall see Him face to face, To thank and praise Him

been a name so dear To this heart of mine, as the name di - vine, The
hon - or and such love, As the bless-ed name, let us all ac-claim,That
for His won-drous grace, Which He gave to me, when He made me free, The

CHORUS

pre-cious, pre-cious name of Je - sus.
won-drous, glo-rious name of Je - sus.   Je-sus is the sweet-est name I
bless-ed Son of God named Je-sus.

know, And He's just the same as His love - ly name, And that's the rea - son

Rall.

why I love Him so; Oh, Je - sus is the sweet-est name I know.

8 Joy Unspeakable

B. E. W.

B. E. Warren

1. I have found His grace is all complete, He sup - pli - eth ev - 'ry need;
2. I have found the pleasure I once craved, It is joy and peace with - in;
3. I have found that hope so bright and clear, Liv - ing in the realm of grace;
4. I have found the joy no tongue can tell, How its waves of glo - ry roll!

While I sit and learn at Je - sus' feet, I am free, yes, free in - deed....
What a wondrous blessing! I am saved From the aw - ful gulf of sin....
Oh, the Saviour's presence is so near, I can see His smil - ing face....
It is like a great o'er-flow-ing well, Springing up with - in my soul....

CHORUS.

It is joy un - speak - a - ble and full of glo - ry, Full of glo - ry, full of glo - ry; It is joy un - speak - a - ble and full of glo - ry, Oh, the half has nev - er yet been told.

Love Lifted Me

9

James Rowe

Howard E. Smith

1. I was sink-ing deep in sin, Far from the peaceful shore,
2. All my heart to Him I give, Ev-er to Him I cling,
3. Souls in dan-ger, look a-bove, Je-sus com-plete-ly saves;

Ver-y
In His
He will

deep-ly stained within, Sink-ing to rise no more;
bless-ed pres-ence live, Ev-er His prais-es sing,
lift you by His love Out of the an-gry waves,

But the Mas-ter
Love so might-y
He's the Mas-ter

of the sea Heard my de-spair-ing cry, From the wa-ters lift-ed me,
and so true Mer-its my soul's best songs, Faith-ful, lov-ing ser-vice, too,
of the sea, Bil-lows His will o-bey; He your Sav-ior wants to be—

CHORUS

Now safe am I. Love lift-ed me! Love lift-ed me!
To Him be-longs.
Be saved to-day. e-ven me! e-ven me!

1 When noth-ing else could help, Love lift-ed me, **2** Love lift-ed me.

10 I Am Resolved

Palmer Hartsough

J. H. Fillmore

1. I am re-solved no long-er to lin-ger, Charmed by the
2. I am re-solved to go to the Sav-ior, Leav-ing my
3. I am re-solved to fol-low the Sav-ior, Faith-ful and
4. I am re-solved to en-ter the king-dom, Leav-ing the
5. I am re-solved, and who will go with me? Come, friends, with-

world's de-light; Things that are high-er, things that are no-bler,
sin and strife; He is the true One, He is the just One,
true each day, Heed what He say-eth, do what He will-eth,
paths of sin; Friends may op-pose me, foes may be-set me,
out de-lay, Taught by the Bi-ble, led by the Spir-it,

CHORUS

These have al-lured my sight. I will has-ten to Him,
He hath the words of life.
He is the liv-ing way.
Still will I en-ter in.
We'll walk the heav'n-ly way. I will has-ten, has-ten to Him,

Has-ten so glad and free, has-ten glad and free,

Je - sus, great-est, high-est, I will come to Thee.
Je - sus, Je - sus,

I Must Tell Jesus

11

E. A. H.

Elisha A. Hoffman

1. I must tell Je-sus all of my tri - als; I can - not bear these
2. I must tell Je-sus all of my trou - bles; He is a kind, com-
3. Tempted and tried, I need a great Sav - ior, One who can help my
4. O how the world to e - vil al - lures me! O how my heart is

bur-dens a - lone; In my dis-tress He kind-ly will help me;
pas-sion-ate friend; If I but ask Him, He will de - liv - er;
bur - dens to bear; I must tell Je - sus, I must tell Je -sus;
tempt-ed to sin! I must tell Je - sus, and He will help me

CHORUS

He ev - er loves and cares for His own.
Make of my trou - bles quick - ly an end.
He all my cares and sor-rows will share.
O - ver the world the vic-t'ry to win.

I must tell Je - sus!

I must tell Je-sus! I can-not bear my burdens a - lone; I must tell

Je-sus! I must tell Je-sus! Je-sus can help me, Je-sus a - lone.

12 In the Garden

C. A. M.

C. Austin Miles

1. I come to the gar-den a-lone, While the dew is still on the
2. He speaks, and the sound of His voice Is so sweet, the birds hush their
3. I'd stay in the gar-den with Him, Tho' the night a-round me be

ros - es; And the voice I hear, Fall-ing on my ear, The
sing - ing, And the mel - o - dy That He gave to me, With-
fall - ing, But He bids me go; Thru the voice of woe, His

CHORUS

Son of God dis-clos - es.
in my heart is ring - ing. And He walks with me and He
voice to me is call - ing.

talks with me, And He tells me I am His own, And the

joy we share as we tar - ry there, None oth-er has ev - er known.

Fill My Cup, Lord

13

R. B.

Richard Blanchard

1. Like the wo-man at the well I was seeking For things that could not
2. There are mil-lions in this world who are craving The pleasure earthly
3. So, my bro-ther, if the things this world gave you Leave hungers that won't

sat - is - fy. And then I heard my Sav-ior speaking: "Draw from my
things afford. But none can match the wond'rous treasure ___ that I
pass a - way, My bless-ed Lord will come and save you ___ if you

CHORUS

well that nev-er shall run dry!" ___ Fill my cup, Lord, I lift it
find in Je-sus Christ, my Lord. ___
kneel to Him and hum-bly pray: ___

up, Lord ___ Come and quench this thirsting of my soul. Bread of hea-ven,

feed me till I want no more, Fill my cup, fill it up and make me whole.

14   Room at the Cross for You

I. F. S. *with feeling*

Ira F. Stanphill

1. The cross up - on which Je - sus died Is a shel - ter in which we can hide, And its grace so free is suf - fi - cient for me, And deep is its foun - tain; as wide as the sea.

2. Tho' mil - lions have found Him a friend And have turned from the sins they have sinned, The Sav - ior still waits to o - pen the gates, And wel - come a sin - ner be - fore it's too late.

3. The hand of my Sav - ior is strong And the love of my Sav - ior is long, Thro' sun - shine or rain thro' loss or in gain, The blood flows from Cal - v'ry to cleanse ev - 'ry stain.

CHORUS

There's room at the cross for you, There's room at the cross for you, Tho' mil - lions have come There's still room for one, Yes, there's room at the cross for you.

Mansion Over the Hilltop

15

I. S.

Ira Stanphill

1. I'm sat-is-fied with just a cot-tage be-low, A lit-tle sil-ver,
2. Tho of-ten tempt-ed, tor - ment-ed and test-ed And like the proph-et,
3. Don't think me poor or de - sert-ed or lone-ly, I'm not dis-cour-aged,

and a lit - tle gold; But in that cit - y where the ransomed will shine,
my pil-low a stone; And tho I find here no permanent dwell-ing,
I'm Heav-en bound; I'm just a pil-grim in search of a cit-y,

CHORUS

I want a gold one that's sil - ver lined.
I know He'll give me a mansion my own.   I've got a man-sion just
I want a man-sion, a harp and a crown.

o - ver the hill-top, In that bright land where we'll never grow old, And some-day

yon-der we will nev-er-more wan-der But walk on streets that are purest gold.

16   The Way that He Loves

W. E. M.

W. Elmo Mercer

1. The way that He loves is as fair as the day, That bless-es my
2. The way that He loves is as deep as the sea, His spir-it shall

way with light. The way that He loves is as soft as the
by my stay. The way that He loves is as pure as a

breeze, Ca-ress-ing the trees at night. So ten-der and pre-cious is
rose, Much sweet-er He grows each day. His peace hov-ers near like a

He, Con-tent-ed with Je-sus I'll be. The way that He
dove, I know there's a heav-en a-bove. To Je-sus I

loves is so thrill-ing be-cause His love reach-es e-ven me.
cling life's a won-der-ful thing Be-cause of the way He loves.

Lonely Road! Up Calvary's Way 17

W. E. M.

W. Elmo Mercer

1. Up the Cal - va - ry way, Went my Sav-iour one day, With a heart that
2. Oh, the way Je - sus trod, Made a pathway to God, We can trav - el

was break-ing in two, Crown of thorns that He wore, Heav - y
the Cal - v'ry way, too, For this Je - sus in love, Leads to

Cross that He bore, It was all for me and for you.
Heav - en a - bove. If we fol - low His steps and are true.

CHORUS

Lone-ly road, Calv'ry's way was a lone-ly road to Je - sus that day;

Heav-y load, He bore our sins on that lone-ly road, Up Cal - va-ry's way.

18 Rise and Be Healed

M. B.

Milton Bourgeois

1. Has fear and doubt come a-gainst your mind? Has your faith been
2. If by faith you reach out to Him, He will meet your

sore - ly tried? Lift up your eyes here com - eth your
ev - 'ry need. He will re - spond to the cry of your

CHORUS

help! It is Je - sus, for you He has died! Rise and be
heart, He will touch you and set you free! Rise and be

healed in the name of Je - sus. Let faith a -

rise in your soul! Rise and be healed in the name of

Je - sus He will make you ev - 'ry whit whole!

Beautiful Isle

Jessie B. Pounds

J. S. Fearis
Arr. by John T. Benson, Jr.

19

1. Some-where the sun is shin-ing, Some-where the song-birds dwell; Hush, then,
2. Some-where the day is long-er, Some-where the task is done; Some-where
3. Some-where the load is lift - ed, Close by an o - pen gate; Some-where

CHORUS

thy sad re - pin - ing, God lives and all is well. Some - where,
the heart is strong-er, Some-where the vic - t'ries won.
the clouds are rift - ed, Some-where the an - gels wait. Somewhere, beau-ti - ful,

Some - where, Beau-ti - ful Isle of some - where! Land of the
beau - ti - ful Isle,

true where we live a - new, Beau - ti - ful Isle of Some-where!

20 Count Your Blessings

Rev. Johnson Oatman, Jr.   E. O. Excell

1. When up-on life's bil-lows you are tem - pest - tossed, When you are dis-
2. Are you ev - er burdened with a load of care? Does the cross seem
3. When you look at oth - ers with their lands and gold, Think that Christ has
4. So, a - mid the con-flict, whether great or small, Do not be dis-

cour-aged, thinking all is lost, Count your man - y blessings, name them
heav - y you are called to bear? Count your man - y blessings, ev - 'ry
prom-ised you His wealth un - told; Count your man - y blessings, mon - ey
cour-aged, God is o - - ver all; Count your man - y blessings, an - gels

one by one, And it will sur - prise you what the Lord hath done.
doubt will fly, And you will be sing-ing as the days go by.
can - - not buy Your re-ward in heav-en, nor your home on high.
will at - - tend, Help and comfort give you to your jour - ney's end.

CHORUS

Count your blessings, Name them one by one; Count your
Count your man-y blessings, Name them one by one; Count your man - y

bless-ings, See what God hath done; Count your bless-ings,
bless-ings, See what God hath done; Count your man-y bless-ings,

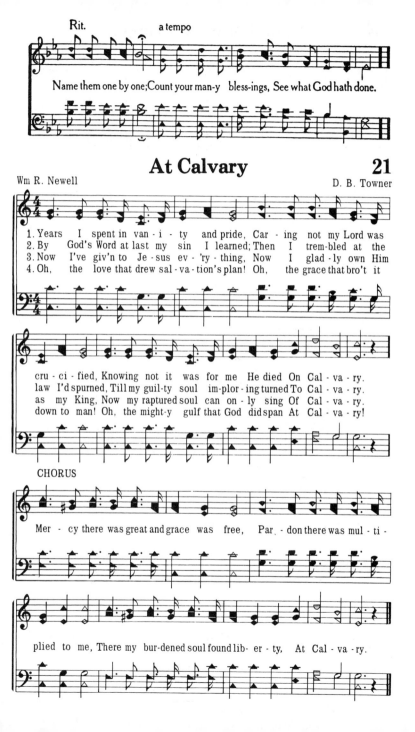

Name them one by one; Count your man-y bless-ings, See what God hath done.

At Calvary

21

Wm. R. Newell

D. B. Towner

1. Years I spent in van-i-ty and pride, Car-ing not my Lord was
2. By God's Word at last my sin I learned; Then I trem-bled at the
3. Now I've giv'n to Je-sus ev-'ry-thing, Now I glad-ly own Him
4. Oh, the love that drew sal-va-tion's plan! Oh, the grace that bro't it

cru-ci-fied, Knowing not it was for me He died On Cal-va-ry.
law I'd spurned, Till my guil-ty soul im-plor-ing turned To Cal-va-ry.
as my King, Now my raptured soul can on-ly sing Of Cal-va-ry.
down to man! Oh, the might-y gulf that God did span At Cal-va-ry!

CHORUS

Mer-cy there was great and grace was free, Par-don there was mul-ti-

plied to me, There my bur-dened soul found lib-er-ty, At Cal-va-ry.

22 If That Isn't Love

D. R.

Dottie Rambo

1. He left the splen-dor of Heav-en ____ Knowing His des - ti-
2. E - ven in death He re - mem-bered ____ The thief hanging by His

ny ____ Was the lone-ly hill of Gol-goth-a ____ There to lay
side ____ ____ He spoke with love and compassion ____ Then He took

CHORUS Tacet.

down His life for me. ____ If that is - n't love ____ The
him to Par - a - dise. ____

o - cean is dry; ____ There's no stars in the sky ____ And the sparrow ____

Tacet

can't fly! ____ If that is - n't love ____ Then Heav-en's a

myth ___ There's no feeling like this ___ If that is-n't love. ___

At the Cross

Isaac Watts

R. E. Hudson

1. A - las, and did my Sav-ior bleed, And did my Sovereign die; Would He de-
2. Was it for crimes that I have done, He groaned upon the tree? A - maz - ing
3. Well might the sun in darkness hide, And shut His glories in, When Christ, the
4. But drops of grief can ne'er re-pay The debt of love I owe; Here, Lord, I

CHORUS

vote that sa - cred head For such a worm as I?
pit - y, grace unknown! And love beyond degree! At the cross, at the cross where I
might-y Mak - er, died for man the creature's sin.
give my-self a-way, 'Tis all that I can do!

first saw the light, And the burden of my heart rolled away, It was
rolled a-way,

there by faith I received my sight, And now I am hap-py all the day!

24 Statue of Liberty

N. E.

Neil Enloe

1. In New _____ York har - bor stands a la - dy, with a
2. On lone - ly Gol - goth - a stood a cross, _____ with my

torch raised to the sky; _____ And all who see ___ her,
Lord raised to the sky; _____ And all who kneel ___ there

know she stands for _____ Lib - er - ty for you and
live for - ev - er as all the saved can tes - ti -

me. _____ I'm so proud to be called an A - mer - i - can, ___
fy. _____ I'm so glad to be called _____ a Chris - tian, ___
CODA Oh, the cross is my stat - ue of lib - er - ty,

_____ To be named with the brave and the free; _____ I will
_____ To be named with the ran - somed and whole; _____ As the
It was there that my soul was set free; _____ Un - a -

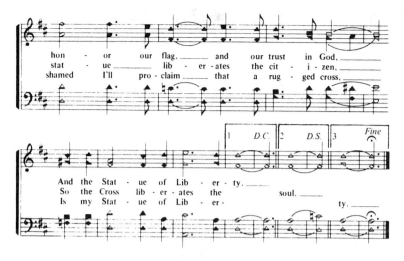

hon — or our flag, _____ and our trust in God,
stat — ue _____ lib — er — ates the cit — i — zen,
shamed I'll pro — claim _____ that a rug — ged cross, _____

1 | D.C. | 2 | D.S. | 3 | *Fine*

And the Stat — ue of Lib — er — ty. _____
So the Cross lib — er — ates the soul. _____
Is my Stat — ue of Lib — er — ty. _____

Leaning on the Everlasting Arms 25

E. A. Hoffman

A. J. Showalter

1 { What a fel — low-ship, what a joy di — vine, Lean-ing on the ev — er-
{ What a bless — ed-ness, what a peace is mine, Lean-ing on the ev — er-
2 { O how sweet to walk in this pil-grim way, Lean-ing on the ev — er-
{ O how bright the path grows from day to day, Lean-ing on the ev — er-
3 { What have I to dread, what have I to fear, Lean-ing on the ev — er-
{ I have bless- ed peace with my Lord so near, Lean-ing on the ev — er-

Chorus

last — ing arms;   Lean — ing, lean — ing,
last — ing arms. Lean-ing on Je — sus, lean-ing on Je — sus,

Safe and se-cure from all a-larms;
(Omit . . . .) Leaning on the ev — er-last-ing arms.

26 To God Be the Glory

Fanny J. Crosby

William H. Doane

1. To God be the glo-ry, great things He hath done; So loved He the
2. O per-fect re-demp-tion, the pur-chase of blood, To ev-'ry be-
3. Great things He hath taught us, great things He hath done, And great our re-

world that He gave us His Son, Who yield-ed His life an a-
liev-er the prom-ise of God; The vil-est of-fend-er who
joic-ing thro' Je-sus, the Son; But pur-er and high-er, and

tone-ment for sin, And o-pened the life-gate that all may go in.
tru-ly be-lieves, That mo-ment from Je-sus a par-don re-ceives.
great-er will be Our won-der, our vic-t'ry when Je-sus we see.

CHORUS

Praise the Lord, praise the Lord, Let the earth hear His voice! Praise the Lord,

praise the Lord, Let the peo - ple re - joice! O come to the Fa - ther, thru

Je - sus, the Son, And give Him the glo - ry, great things He hath done. A - men.

Blessed Assurance 27

Fanny J. Crosby

Mrs. J. F. Knapp

1. Blessed as-surance, Je-sus is mine! O what a foretaste of glory divine! Heir of sal-
2. Perfect submission, perfect delight, Vi-sions of rapture now burst on my sight; Angels de-
3. Perfect submission, all is at rest, I in my Savior am happy and blest; Watching and

FINE CHORUS

va - tion, purchase of God, Born of His Spirit, washed in His blood.
scending, bring from above, Echoes of mercy, whispers of love. This is my sto - ry,
wait-ing, looking a - bove, Filled with His goodness, lost in His love.

D. S.-Praising my Savior all the day long.

D.S.

this is my song, Praising my Savior all the day long; This is my story, this is my song,

28 Follow Me

I. F. S.

Ira F. Stanphill

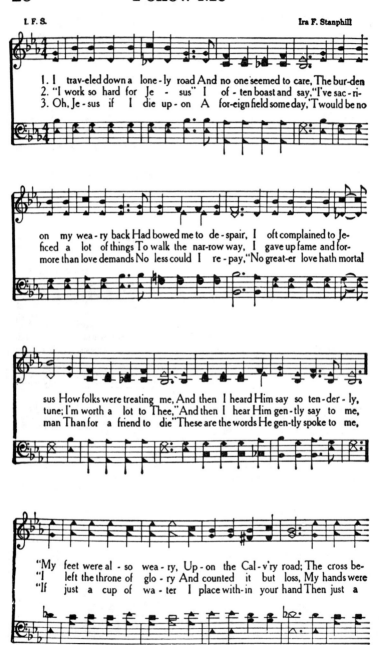

1. I trav-eled down a lone-ly road And no one seemed to care, The bur-den
2. "I work so hard for Je - sus" I of - ten boast and say, "I've sac - ri-
3. Oh, Je - sus if I die up - on A for-eign field some day, 'T would be no

on my wea - ry back Had bowed me to de - spair, I oft complained to Je-
ficed a lot of things To walk the nar-row way, I gave up fame and for-
more than love demands No less could I re - pay, "No great-er love hath mortal

sus How folks were treating me, And then I heard Him say so ten-der - ly,
tune; I'm worth a lot to Thee," And then I hear Him gen-tly say to me,
man Than for a friend to die "These are the words He gen-tly spoke to me,

"My feet were al - so wea - ry, Up - on the Cal - v'ry road; The cross be-
"I left the throne of glo - ry And counted it but loss, My hands were
"If just a cup of wa - ter I place with-in your hand Then just a

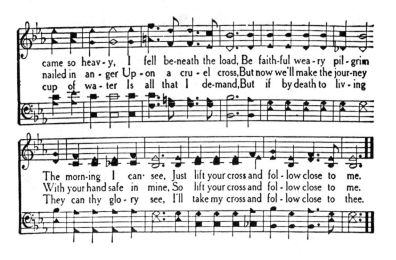

came so heav-y, I fell be-neath the load, Be faith-ful wea-ry pil-grim
nailed in an-ger Up-on a cru-el cross, But now we'll make the jour-ney
cup of wa-ter Is all that I de-mand, But if by death to liv-ing

The morn-ing I can see, Just lift your cross and fol-low close to me.
With your hand safe in mine, So lift your cross and fol-low close to me.
They can thy glo-ry see, I'll take my cross and fol-low close to thee.

Hand in Hand with Jesus   29

Rev. Johnson Oatman, Jr.   L. D. Huffstutler

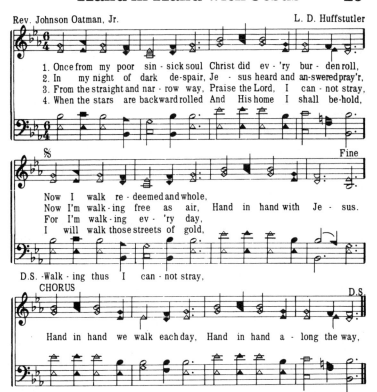

1. Once from my poor sin-sick soul Christ did ev-'ry bur-den roll,
2. In my night of dark de-spair, Je-sus heard and an-swered pray'r,
3. From the straight and nar-row way, Praise the Lord, I can-not stray,
4. When the stars are backward rolled And His home I shall be-hold,

Now I walk re-deemed and whole,
Now I'm walk-ing free as air, Hand in hand with Je-sus.
For I'm walk-ing ev-'ry day,
I will walk those streets of gold,

D.S. -Walk-ing thus I can-not stray,

CHORUS

Hand in hand we walk each day, Hand in hand a-long the way,

30 What a Day That Will Be

J. H.

Jim Hill

1. There is com-ing a-day when no heart-aches shall come, No more
2. There'll be no sor-row there, no more bur-dens to bear, No more

clouds in the sky, no more tears to dim the eye; All is peace
sick-ness, no pain, no more part-ing o-ver there; And for-ev-

for-ev-er-more on that hap-py, gold-en shore, What a day, glo-ri-ous
er I will be with the One who died for me,

day that will be.

CHORUS

What a day that will be when my Je-sus
I shall see, And I look up-on His face, the One who saved me

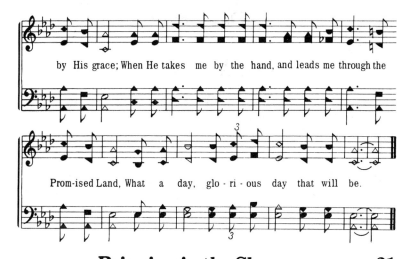

by His grace; When He takes me by the hand, and leads me through the

Prom-ised Land, What a day, glo-ri-ous day that will be.

Bringing in the Sheaves   31

Knowles Shaw

George A. Minor

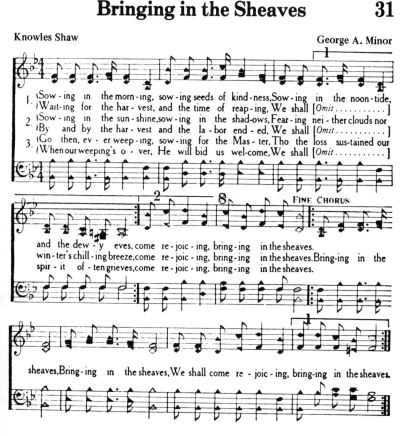

1. {Sow - ing in the morn-ing, sow-ing seeds of kind-ness,Sow-ing in the noon-tide,
   {Wait-ing for the har - vest, and the time of reap-ing, We shall [Omit . . . .]
2. {Sow - ing in the sun-shine,sow-ing in the shad-ows,Fear-ing nei - ther clouds nor
   {By and by the har - vest and the la - bor end - ed, We shall [Omit . . . .]
3. {Go then, ev - er weep-ing, sow-ing for the Mas - ter, Tho the loss sus-tained our
   {When our weeping's o - ver, He will bid us wel-come,We shall [Omit . . . .]

FINE CHORUS

and the dew - y eves, come re - joic - ing, bring-ing in the sheaves.
win - ter's chill-ing breeze,come re - joic - ing, bring-ing in the sheaves.Bring-ing in the
spir - it of - ten grieves,come re - joic - ing, bring-ing in the sheaves.

sheaves,Bring-ing in the sheaves,We shall come re - joic-ing, bring-ing in the sheaves.

32 Come and Dine

Words and melody by C. C. Widmeyer

S. H. Bolton

1. Je - sus has a ta - ble spread Where the saints of God are fed,
2. The dis - ci - ples came to land, Thus o - bey - ing Christ's command,
3. Soon the Lamb will take His bride To be ev - er at His side,

He in - vites His chos-en peo - ple "Come and dine;" With His man - na
For the Mas - ter called un - to them, "Come and dine;" There they found their
All the host of Heav- en will as - sem-bled be; O, 'twill be a

He doth feed And sup-plies our ev - 'ry need: O 'tis sweet to sup with
hearts' desire, Bread and fish up - on the fire; Thus He sat - is - fies the
glo-rious sight, All the saints in spot-less white; And with Je - sus they will

CHORUS

Je - sus all the time!
hun - gry ev - 'ry time. "Come and dine," the Mas - ter call - eth, "Come and
feast e - ter - nal - ly.

dine;"
O come and dine;

You may feast at Je - sus' ta - ble all the

time; O come and dine; He who fed the mul - ti - tude, Turned the
wa - ter in - to wine, To the hun - gry call-eth now, "Come and dine."

O Come, Angel Band 33

Jefferson Hascall

W. B. Bradbury

1 { My lat - est sun is sink - ing fast, My race is near - ly run,
{ My strong - est tri - als now are past, My tri - umph is be - gun!

2 { I know I'm near - ing ho - ly ranks Of friends and kin - dred dear;
{ I brush the dew of Jordan's banks, The cross - ing must be near;

3 { I've al - most gained my heav'n - ly home, My spir - it loud - ly sings;
{ The ho - ly ones, be - hold, they come! I hear the noise of wings,

4 { O bear my long - ing heart to Him Who bled and died for me;
{ Whose blood now clean - ses from all sin, And gives me vic - to - ry.

Refrain f

O come, an-gel band, come, and around me stand, O bear me a - way on your

1 2

snow - y wings To my im - mor - tal home my im - mor - tal home.

34 Whispering Hope

Alice Hawthorne

Arranged by John T. Benson, Jr.

1. Soft as the voice of an an-gel, Breathing a les-son un-heard,
2. If in the dusk of the twi-light, Dim be the re-gion a-far,
3. Hope, as an an-chor so stead-fast, Rends the dark veil for the soul,

Hope with a gen-tle per-sua-sion Whis-pers her com-fort-ing word:
Will not the deep-en-ing dark-ness Bright-en the glim-mer-ing star?
Whith-er the Mas-ter has en-tered, Rob-bing the grave of its goal;

Wait till the dark-ness is o-ver, Wait till the tem-pest is done,
Then when the night is up-on us, Why should the heart sink a-way?
Come then, O come, glad fru-i-tion, Come to my sad, wea-ry heart;

Hope for the sun-shine to-mor-row, Aft-er the show-er is
When the dark mid-night is o-ver, Watch for the break-ing of
Come, O Thou blest hope of glo-ry, Nev-er, O nev-er de-

CHORUS

gone. Whis - - - per - ing hope, O how
day.
part. Whis-per-ing hope, Whis-per-ing hope,

Wel-come thy voice, Mak - - ing my
Wel-come thy voice, O how wel-come thy voice, Mak-ing my heart,

heart in its sor - - row re-joice.
mak-ing my heart, in its sor-row, its sor-rows re-joice.

How Beautiful Heaven Must Be   35

Mrs. A. S. Bridgewater

A. P. Bland

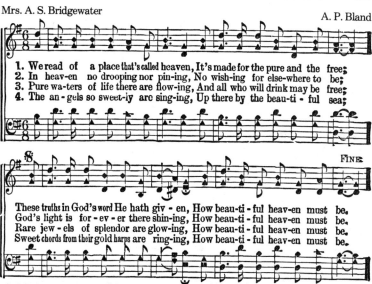

1. We read of a place that's called heaven, It's made for the pure and the free;
2. In heav-en no drooping nor pin-ing, No wish-ing for else-where to be;
3. Pure wa-ters of life there are flow-ing, And all who will drink may be free;
4. The an-gels so sweet-ly are sing-ing, Up there by the beau-ti - ful sea;

FINE

These truths in God's word He hath giv - en, How beau-ti - ful heav-en must be.
God's light is for - ev - er there shin-ing, How beau-ti - ful heav-en must be.
Rare jew - els of splendor are glow-ing, How beau-ti - ful heav-en must be.
Sweet chords from their gold harps are ring-ing, How beau-ti - ful heav-en must be.

D. S. Fair ha-ven of rest for the wear - y, How beau-ti - ful heav-en must be.

REFRAIN.

D. S.

How beau-ti - ful heav-en must be, must be, Sweet home of the hap - py and free;

36
Learning to Lean

J.S.

John Stallings

I'm learn-ing to lean, learn-ing to lean, Learn-ing to

lean ___ on Je - sus; Find-ing more pow-er

than I'd ev - er dreamed; I'm learn-ing to lean on

Last time to

VERSE

Je - sus. ___

1. The joy I can't ex-plain ___
2. Sometimes ___ we can be ___
3. ___ Sad, ___ bro - ken heart-ed,
4. There's glo - ri - ous vic-t'ry

___ like the man ___ who said,
fills ___ my soul, Since ___ the day I
My life is full now,
___ so oft - en ___ I've knelt, And ___ I've found
___ each day now ___ for me, ___ I found

made Je - sus my King;___ His bless - ed ___ Ho - ly
I have ev - 'ry-thing;___ But there is ___ a strong
God's peace so se - rene;___ ___ And all ___ that He
His peace so se - rene;___ ___ He helps ___ me with each

Spir - it ___ is lead-ing my way, He's ___ teach-ing and I'm
Rock ___ ___ in Je - sus, my Lord; Thro' my tri - als I've been
asks ___ is a child - like trust, And a heart ___ that is
task ___ ___ if on - ly I'll ask; Ev - 'ry day now I'm ___

D. S.

learn-ing ___ to lean. ___ I'm Je - sus. ___

Amazing Grace

37

John Newton

American Melody

1. A - maz-ing grace how sweet the sound; That saved a wretch like me!
2. 'Twas grace that taught my heart to fear, And grace my fears re-lieved;
3. Thru man - y dan - gers, toils and snares, I have al - read - y come;
4. When we've been there ten thousand years, Bright shining as the sun;

I once was lost but now am found, Was blind but now I see.
How pre-cious did that grace ap-pear, The hour I first be - lieved.
'Tis grace that bro't me safe thus far, And grace will lead me home.
We've no less days to sing God's praise, Than when we first be - gun.

38 Bring all Your Needs to the Altar

D. R.

Dottie Rambo

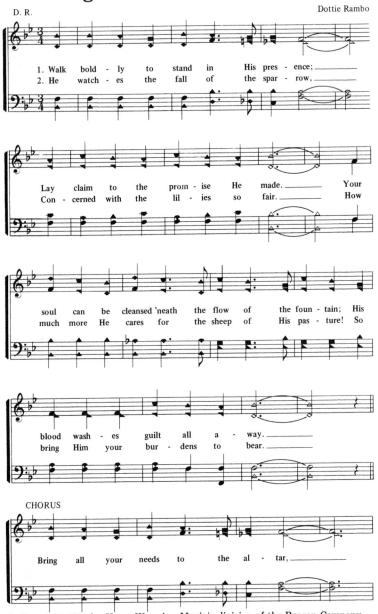

1. Walk bold - ly to stand in His pres - ence;
2. He watch - es the fall of the spar - row,

Lay claim to the prom - ise He made._____ Your
Con - cerned with the lil - ies so fair._____ How

soul can be cleansed 'neath the flow of the foun - tain; His
much more He cares for the sheep of His pas - ture! So

blood wash - es guilt all a - way._____
bring Him your bur - dens to bear._____

CHORUS

Bring all your needs to the al - tar,_____

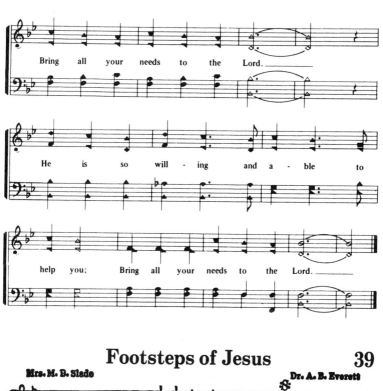

Bring all your needs to the Lord.

He is so will - ing and a - ble to

help you; Bring all your needs to the Lord.

Footsteps of Jesus

39

Mrs. M. B. Slade

Dr. A. B. Everett

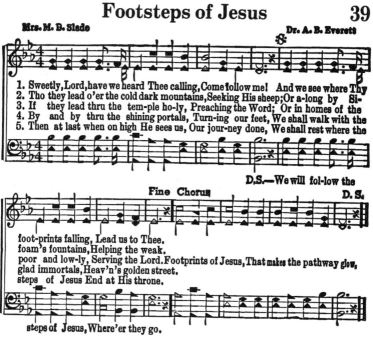

1. Sweetly, Lord, have we heard Thee calling, Come follow me! And we see where Thy
2. Tho they lead o'er the cold dark mountains, Seeking His sheep; Or a-long by Si-
3. If they lead thru the tem-ple ho-ly, Preaching the Word; Or in homes of the
4. By and by thru the shining portals, Turn-ing our feet, We shall walk with the
5. Then at last when on high He sees us, Our jour-ney done, We shall rest where the

D.S.—We will fol-low the

Fine Chorus

D. S.

foot-prints falling, Lead us to Thee.
foam's fountains, Helping the weak.
poor and low-ly, Serving the Lord. Footprints of Jesus, That makes the pathway glow,
glad immortals, Heav'n's golden street.
steps of Jesus End at His throne.

steps of Jesus, Where'er they go.

40 I'm Standing on the Solid Rock

H. L.

Harold Lane

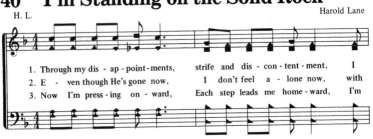

1. Through my dis - ap - point - ments, strife and dis - con - tent - ment, I
2. E - ven though He's gone now, I don't feel a - lone now, with
3. Now I'm press - ing on - ward, Each step leads me home - ward, I'm

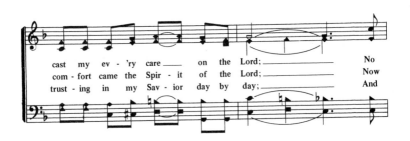

cast my ev - 'ry care_____ on the Lord;_____ No
com - fort came the Spir - it of the Lord;_____ Now
trust - ing in my Sav - ior day by day;_____ And

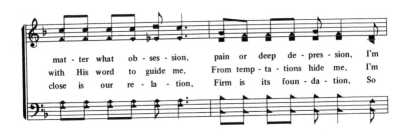

mat - ter what ob - ses - sion, pain or deep de - pres - sion, I'm
with His word to guide me, From temp - ta - tions hide me, I'm
close is our re - la - tion, Firm is its foun - da - tion, So

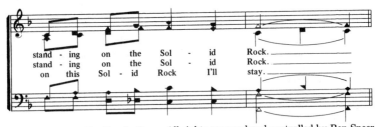

stand - ing on the Sol - id Rock._____
stand - ing on the Sol - id Rock._____
on this Sol - id Rock I'll stay._____

CHORUS

I'm stand - ing on the Rock of A - ges,
Stand-ing on the Rock, On the Rock of A - ges,

Safe _____ from all the storm that ra - ges,
Safe from ev - 'ry storm, All the storm that ra - ges,

Rich _____ but not from Sa - tan's wa - ges, I'm
Rich in love, I'm rich, Not from Sa - tan's wa - ges,

stand - ing on the Sol - id Rock. _____

I'm Going Home
41

Wm. D. Hunter, D. D.   Arr. by Rev. W. McDonald

1 { My heav-'nly home is bright and fair, No pain nor death, can en - ter there; }
  { Its glitt-'ring tow'rs the sun out shine; That heav'nly mansion shall be mine. }
CHO. { I'm go-ing home, I'm go - ing home, I'm go-ing home to die no more; }
     { To die no more, to die no more, I'm go-ing home to die no more. }

42 I Came on Business for the King

J. H.

Joel Hemphill

1. Some - one here needs help and I can't do much,
2. Let's not hur - ry through and close up our hearts,

But if we keep on prais - ing He'll send His touch;
With pro - grams so well - planned, we leave out His part;

Heal - ing for bod - y and soul He will
Let's pause for a mo - ment, to His Spir - it to

bring, I came on bus - 'ness for the King.
cling, I came on bus - 'ness for the King.

CHORUS

I came on bus - 'ness for the King, He

told me to smile _____ and He told me to sing; _____

_____ I can't just stand here and do my own

thing. I came on bus - 'ness for the King. _____

Where Could I Go? 43

J. B. C.   J. B. Coats

1. Liv - ing be-low in this old sin - ful world, Hardly a com - fort can af - ford;
2. Neighbors are kind, I love them ev - 'ry one, We get a - long in sweet accord;
3. Life here is grand with friends I love so dear, Comfort I get from God's own word;

Cho.- Where could I go, O where could I go, Seeking a ref - uge for my soul?

D. C. for Chorus

Striving a - lone to face temp - tation sore,
But when my soul needs manna from above, Where could I go but to the Lord?
Yet when I face the chill - ing hand of death,

Need-ing a friend to save me in the end, Where could I go but to the Lord?

44 It Made News in Heaven
(When I Got Saved)

G. J.

Gordon Jensen

1. It did-n't make the pa-pers in this world when I prayed
2. Not long a-go a beg-gar, now a child of the

through; It did-n't seem to mat-ter to all, but
King, This old world just shrugged its shoul-ders, it did-n't

just a few; But in the gold-en streets of glo-ry,
mean a thing; But it was God's ap-pro-val,

cel-e-bra-tion ban-ners waved; It made news in Heav-en
my spir-it real-ly craved; It made news in Heav-en

CHORUS

when I got saved! An-gels were re-joic-ing, hal-le-

lu - jahs rang, When Je - sus touched my life and I was changed.

Ev - 'ry - one in glo - ry's realm knew my name was writ - ten

down. It made news in Heav - en, when I got saved.

Just as I Am

45

Charlotte Elliott   William B. Bradbury

1. Just as I am, with-out one plea   But that Thy blood was shed for me,
2. Just as I am, and wait - ing not   To rid my soul of one dark blot,
3. Just as I am, tho tossed a - bout   With many a con-flict, many a doubt,
4. Just as I am, poor, wretch- ed, blind—Sight, rich-es, heal-ing of the mind,
5. Just as I am, Thou wilt receive, Wilt wel-come, par-don, cleanse, re-lieve.

And that Thou bidd'st me come to Thee,   O Lamb of God, I come! I come!
To Thee, whose blood can cleanse each spot, O Lamb of God, I come! I come!
Fight-ings and fears, with - in, with-out,   O Lamb of God, I come! I come!
Yea, all I need in Thee to find   O Lamb of God, I come! I come!
Be-cause Thy prom- ise I be-lieve,   O Lamb of God, I come! I come!

46
Rise Again

D. H.

Dallas Holm

love ___ for you ___ is still ___ the same, ___ Go a - head and

D.S. to Chorus

bur - y me _____ but ver - y soon ___ I will ___ be free, ___ 'Cause I'll

ground. 3. Go a - head and say I'm dead and gone, But you ___ will see ___

___ that you ___ were wrong. ___ Go a - head, try to hide ___ the

D.S. to Chorus

Son, But all ___ will see ___ that I'm ___ the One! ___ 'Cause I'll

47 All in the Name of Jesus

S. A.

Steve Adams

1. Truth and beau - ty and hap - pi - ness,
2. Care and com - fort, heal - ing and grace,

It's all in the name of Je - sus;

Health and Heav - en, peace and rest, It's
Wel - come, par - don, a hid - ing place,

all in the name of Je - sus; Joy and
Warmth and

glad - ness, for - give - ness, too; Life ev - er -
sun - shine, friend - ship true; Ful - fill - ment and

48 Give Them all to Jesus

Bob Benson, Sr. & P. J.

Phil Johnson

1. Are you tired o' chas - in' _____ pret - ty rain - bows? _____
2. _____ He nev - er said _____ you'd on - ly see sun - shine,

And are you tired o' spin - nin' _____
And He _____ nev - er said _____ there'd

_____ 'round and 'round? _____ Wrap up all the shat-
be no _____ rain; _____ He on - ly prom-

......tered dreams _____ of your _____ life, _____
...... ised a heart full of sing - in', _____

And at the feet of Je - sus lay them down.   Give them
A - bout the ver - y things _____ that once brought pain.

Give them

49 He's as Close as the Mention of His Name

G. J.

Gordon Jensen

1. In the ver - y thought of Je - sus, His
2. — In my hour of strug - gle so

pres - ence can be found, He's as close as the
man - y times I've found, He's as close as the

men - tion of His Name; ____ There is nev - er ____
men - tion of His Name; ____ Just to breathe ____ the

an - y dis - tance ____ be - tween my Lord and
Name of Je - sus can turn ev - 'ry - thing a -

me, He's as close as the men - tion of His Name.
round,

CHORUS

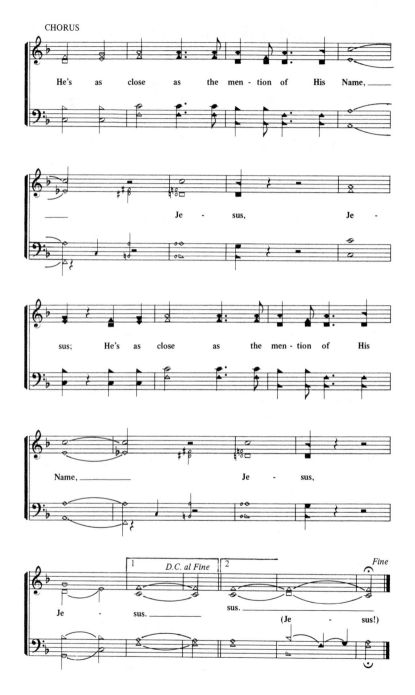

He's as close as the men-tion of His Name, _____ Je - sus, Je - sus; He's as close as the men-tion of His Name, _____ Je - sus, Je - sus. sus. (Je - sus!)

D.C. al Fine

Fine

50 God's Wonderful People

L.W.

REFRAIN:

Lanny Wolfe

I love the thrill that I feel when I get to - geth - er with

God's wonder-ful peo - ple, Love the thrill that I feel when I

get to - geth - er with God's won - der - ful peo - ple; What a

sight just to see all the hap - py fa - ces prais - ing God in heav - en -

ly pla - ces; What a thrill that I feel when I get to - geth - er with

Fine

God's _____ won - der - ful peo - ple. _____

VERSE:

1. Oh, what joy His love _____ af - fords _____ when we meet in one _____
2. It can be just an - y - where _____ two or three are gath -
3. On that great re - un - ion day _____ when our Lord says, "Come _____

ac - cord, _____ And we lift our hearts in praise _____ un - to the Lord; _____
ered there, _____ That the Spir - it of the Lord _____ will be there, too; _____
a - way", _____ And the saints from ev - 'ry land _____ sweep thro' the gates; _____

There's no place I'd ra - ther be than with the ones who've been set free,
There's no fel - low-ship so sweet, _____ there's no thrill that can compete
Join - ing loved ones 'round the throne, at last we'll all be gath-ered home,

D. C.

I'm so glad I'm in God's great _____ big fam - i - ly. _____
With the thrill I feel when - ev - er God's chil - dren meet. _____
That will be the great - est thrill _____ we've ev - er known. _____

51 Consider the Lilies

J. H.

Joel Hemphill

1. Con-sid-er ___ the lil-ies, they don't toil ___ nor spin, And there's ___ not a king with more splen-dor than ___ them; Con-sid-er the spar-rows, they don't plant ___ nor sow, But they're fed ___ by the Mas-ter, who watch-es them grow. ___

2. May I ___ in-tro-duce you ___ to this Friend of mine, Who hangs ___ out the stars, tells the sun ___ when to shine; And kiss-es the flow-ers each ___ morn-ing with dew, But ___ He's ___ not too bus-y to care a-bout you. ___

52   Jesus (He Is the Son of God)

D. L.

Danny Lee

1. ____ The bus - y streets and ____ side - walks, ____ they ____
2. There are foot-prints in the ____ sand a - long the ____
3. Then the air grew cold and the sky turned black as they

sud - den - ly grew still, As a Man came thro' the
Sea of Gal - i - lee Where thou - sands came to
nailed Him to a tree, There He died for ev - 'ry

en - trance of the ci - ty; ____ As He touched and
hear and came to see Him; ____ There He taught of
man and ev - 'ry coun - try; ____ But the price He

healed a ____ blind man ____ with a lit - tle piece of clay,
love and ____ kind - ness, ____ yes. He bro't a bet - ter way,
paid and the blood He shed is ____ chang-ing lives to - day,

With ____ trem-bling lips you could hear the peo - ple say: ____
As He spoke they'd turn and ____ whis - per and they'd say: ____
And with joy and praise you can hear these peo - ple say: ____

CHORUS:

Je - sus, Je - sus, He is the Son of God!

Je - sus, Je - sus, the prec - ious Son of

God! ___ Sweet - est Rose of Shar - on came to set us

free; Je - sus, Je - sus, He's ev - 'ry -

thing to me; Yes, He's all the world ___ to me! ___

53 He Keeps Me Singing

L. B. B.

L. B. Bridgers

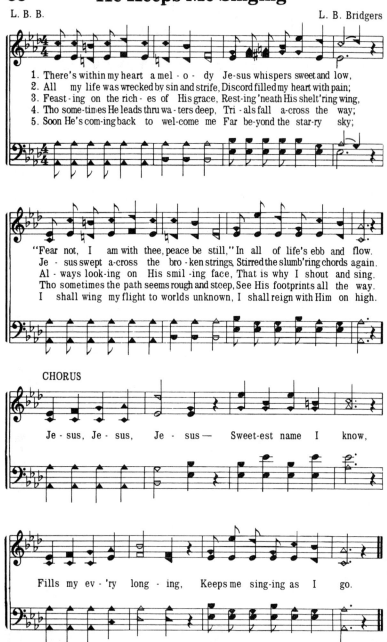

1. There's within my heart a mel - o - dy Je-sus whispers sweet and low,
2. All my life was wrecked by sin and strife, Discord filled my heart with pain;
3. Feast - ing on the rich - es of His grace, Rest-ing 'neath His shelt'ring wing,
4. Tho some-times He leads thru wa - ters deep, Tri - als fall a-cross the way;
5. Soon He's com-ing back to wel-come me Far be-yond the star-ry sky;

"Fear not, I am with thee, peace be still," In all of life's ebb and flow.
Je - sus swept a-cross the bro - ken strings, Stirred the slumb'ring chords again.
Al - ways look-ing on His smil - ing face, That is why I shout and sing.
Tho sometimes the path seems rough and steep, See His footprints all the way.
I shall wing my flight to worlds unknown, I shall reign with Him on high.

CHORUS

Je - sus, Je - sus, Je - sus — Sweet-est name I know,

Fills my ev - 'ry long - ing, Keeps me sing-ing as I go.

God Be with You

54

J. E. Rankin, D. D.

W. G. Tomer

1. God be with you till we meet a-gain, By His coun-sels
2. God be with you till we meet a-gain, 'Neath His wings se-
3. God be with you till we meet a-gain, When life's per - ils
4. God be with you till we meet a-gain, Keep love's ban - ner

guide, up-hold you, With His sheep se - cure-ly fold you, God be
cure-ly hide you, Dai-ly man-na still pro-vide you, God be
thick confound you, Put His arms un - fail-ing round you, God be
float-ing o'er you, Smite death's threat'ning wave be-fore you, God be

with you till we meet a-gain. Till we meet,   till we
                              Till we meet, till we

meet,   Till we meet at Je - sus' feet,   Till we
meet a-gain,   till we meet,

meet,   till we meet,   God be with you till we meet a-gain.
Till we meet, till we meet a-gain,

55 My Savior's Love

C. H. G.

Chas. H. Gabriel

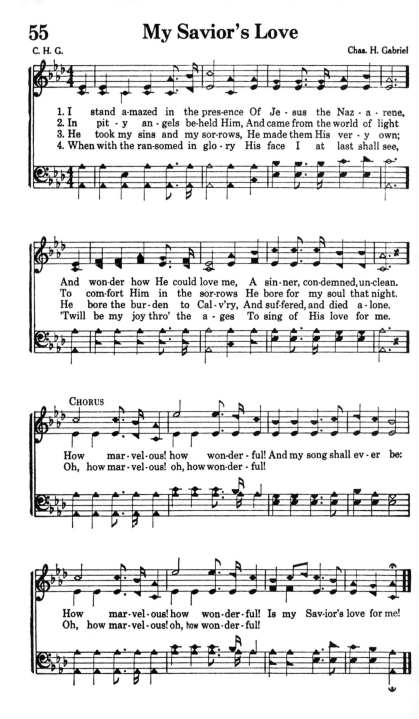

1. I stand a-mazed in the pres-ence Of Je-sus the Naz-a-rene,
2. In pit-y an-gels be-held Him, And came from the world of light
3. He took my sins and my sor-rows, He made them His ver-y own;
4. When with the ran-somed in glo-ry His face I at last shall see,

And won-der how He could love me, A sin-ner, con-demned, un-clean.
To com-fort Him in the sor-rows He bore for my soul that night.
He bore the bur-den to Cal-v'ry, And suf-fered, and died a-lone.
'Twill be my joy thro' the a-ges To sing of His love for me.

CHORUS

How mar-vel-ous! how won-der-ful! And my song shall ev-er be:
Oh, how mar-vel-ous! oh, how won-der-ful!

How mar-vel-ous! how won-der-ful! Is my Sav-ior's love for me!
Oh, how mar-vel-ous! oh, how won-der-ful!

Does Jesus Care?

56

Frank E. Graeff

J. Lincoln Hall

1. Does Je - sus care when my heart is pained Too deep - ly for
2. Does Je - sus care when my way is dark With a name - less
3. Does Je - sus care when I've tried and failed To re - sist some temp -
4. Does Je - sus care when I've said good - bye To the dear - est on

mirth and song; As the bur - dens press, and the cares dis - tress,
dread and fear? As the day - light fades in - to deep night shades,
ta - tion strong; When for my deep grief I find no re - lief,
earth to me, And my sad heart aches till it near - ly breaks,

CHORUS

And the way grows wea - ry and long?
Does He care e - nough to be near?
Tho my tears flow all the night long?
Is it aught to Him? does He see?

O yes, He cares I

know He cares! His heart is touched with my grief; When the days are

wea - ry, the long nights drear - y, I know my Sav - ior cares. (He cares.)

57 The Last Mile of the Way

Johnson Oatman, Jr.

Wm. Edie Marks

1. If I walk in the path-way of du-ty, If I work till the
2. If for Christ I pro-claim the glad sto-ry, If I seek for His
3. Here the dear-est of ties we must sev-er, Tears of sor-row are
4. And if here I have earn-est-ly striv-en And have tried all His

close of the day, I shall see the great King in His beau-ty
sheep gone a-stray, I am sure He will show me His glo-ry
seen ev-'ry day; But no sick-ness, no sigh-ing for-ev-er
will to o-bey, 'Twill en-hance all the rap-ture of heav-en

FINE CHORUS

When I've gone the last mile of the way. When I've gone the last

mile of the way, I will rest at the close of the
the last mile of the way, at the

D. S.

day, And I know there are joys that a-wait me
close of the day,

I Won't Have to Cross Jordan Alone   58

Thomas Ramsey   To my friend V. O. Stamps - C. E. D.   Chas. E. Durham

1. When I come to the riv-er at end-ing of day, When the last winds of
2. Oft-en-times I'm for-sak-en, and wea-ry and sad, When it seems that my
3. Tho the bil-lows of sor-row and trou-ble may sweep, Christ the Sav-ior will

sor-row have blown;........There'll be some-bod-y wait-ing to show me the
friends have all gone;.........There is one tho't that cheers me and makes my heart
care for His own;.........Till the end of the jour-ney, my soul He will

CHORUS

way, I won't have to cross Jor-dan a-lone. I won't have to cross Jordan a-
glad, I won't have to cross Jor-dan a-lone.
keep, I won't have to cross Jor-dan a-lone.   I won't have   to   cross

Solo ad lib.

lone,..............Je-sus died all my sins to a-tone; When the dark-ness I see,
Jor-dan a-lone,   Hum

Parts

He'll be wait-ing for me, I won't have to cross Jor-dan a - lone.
Hum..............

59 The Church in the Wildwood

W. S. P.

Dr. Wm. S. Pitts

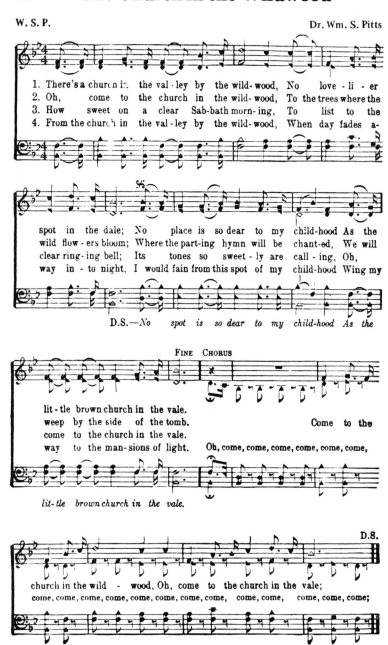

1. There's a church in the val - ley by the wild-wood, No love - li - er
2. Oh, come to the church in the wild-wood, To the trees where the
3. How sweet on a clear Sab-bath morn-ing, To list to the
4. From the church in the val - ley by the wild-wood, When day fades a-

spot in the dale; No place is so dear to my child-hood As the
wild flow-ers bloom; Where the part-ing hymn will be chant-ed, We will
clear ring-ing bell; Its tones so sweet - ly are call - ing, Oh,
way in - to night, I would fain from this spot of my child-hood Wing my

D.S.—No spot is so dear to my child-hood As the

FINE CHORUS

lit - tle brown church in the vale.
weep by the side of the tomb.
come to the church in the vale.   Come to the
way to the man- sions of light.   Oh, come, come, come, come, come, come,

lit- tle brown church in the vale.

D.S.

church in the wild - wood, Oh, come to the church in the vale;
come, come, come, come, come, come, come, come, come, come, come, come, come;

Is That the Old Ship of Zion

60

C. C.

Conrad Cook

1. I was stand - ing on the banks of the riv - er
2. Its hull was bent and bat - tered
3. At the stern of the ship was the cap - tain,
4. As I step on board I'll be leav - ing

Look - ing out o - ver life's trou - bled sea,
From the storms of life, I could see;
I could hear as He called out my name;
All my trou - bles and tri - als be - hind;

When I saw an old ship that was sail - ing.
Waves were rough, but that old ship was sail - ing.
Get on board, it's the old ship of Zi - on,
I'll be safe with Je - sus, the cap - tain,

Is that the old Ship of Zi - on I see?
Is that the old Ship of Zi - on I see?
It will nev - er pass this way a - gain.
Sail - ing out on the old Ship of Zion.

61 Do You Know My Jesus?

V. B. E. & W. F. L.

W. F. (Bill) Lakey
and V. B. (Vep) Ellis

1. Have you a heart that's wea - ry, Tend - ing a load of
2. Where is your heart, oh, pil - grim, What does your light re -
3. Who knows your dis - ap - point - ments, Who knows each time you

care; Are you a soul that's seek - ing Rest from the
veal; Who hears your call for com - fort When naught but
cry; Who un - der-stands your heart - aches, Who dries the

CHORUS

bur - den you bear? Do you know my Je - sus, Do you
sor - row you feel? Do you know
tears from your eyes?

know my friend, Have you heard He
Do you know

loves you, And that He will a - bide till the end?
till the end?

Sunlight

J. W. Van de Venter

W. S. Weeden

1. I wandered in the shades of night, Till Je-sus came to me,
2. Tho' clouds may gath-er in the sky, And billows round me roll,
3. While walk-ing in the light of God, I sweet com-mun-ion find;
4. I cross the wide-ex-tend-ed fields, I jour-ney o'er the plain,
5. Soon I shall see Him as He is, The light that came to me,

And with the sun-light of His love Bid all my dark-ness flee.
How-ev-er dark the world may be, I've sun-light in my soul.
I press with ho-ly vig-or on And leave the world be-hind.
And in the sun-light of His love, I reap the gold-en grain.
Be-hold the brightness of His face, Thro'-out e-ter-ni-ty.

CHORUS.

Sun-light, sun-light in my soul to-day, Sun-light, sun-light
to-day, yes,

all a-long the way; Since the Sav-iour found me, took a-
nar-row way;

way my sin, I have had the sun-light of His love with-in.
load of sin,

63 When I See the Blood

Foote Bros., not copyrighted. Let no one do so. May this song ever be free to be published for the glory of God.

John J. G. F.

1. Christ, our Re-deem-er, died on the cross, Died for the sin-ner,
2. Chief-est of sin-ners Je-sus can save, As He has prom-ised,
3. Judg-ment is com-ing, all will be there, Who have re-ject-ed,
4. O what com-pas-sion, O boundless love, Je-sus hath pow-er,

paid all his due; All who re-ceive Him need nev-er fear,
so will He do; O sin-ner, hear Him, trust in His word,
who have re-fused; O sin-ner, hast-en, let Je-sus in,
Je-sus is true; All who be-lieve are safe from the storm,

Yes, He will pass, will pass o-ver you. When I see the
Then He will pass, will pass o-ver you.
Then God will pass, will pass o-ver you.
O He will pass, will pass o-ver you.

When I

blood, When I see the blood, When I see the
see the blood, When I see the blood, When I

blood, I will pass, I will pass o-ver you.
see the blood, o-ver you.

When They Ring the Golden Bells 64

Dion De Marbelle

1. There's a land be-yond the riv - er, that we call the sweet for-ev - er, And we
2. We shall know no sin nor sor - row, in that hav-en of tomorrow, When our
3. When our days shall know their number, when in death we sweetly slumber, When the

on - ly reach that shore by faith's decree; One by one we'll gain the portals, there to
barque shall sail be-yond the sil - ver sea; We shall only know the blessing of our
King commands the spir-it to be free; Nevermore with anguish laden, we shall

FINE

dwell with the immortals, When they ring the golden bells for you and me.
Father's sweet caressing,
reach that lovely ai-den,

you and me.

D. S. - yond the shining riv-er,

CHORUS

Don't you hear the bells now ringing? don't you hear the an-gels singing? 'Tis the

D.S.

glo-ry hal-le-lu-jah Ju - bi - lee, In that far-off sweet for-ev-er, just be-
Ju-bi-lee,

65 What a Savior

M. P. D.

Marvin P. Dalton

1. Once I was stray-ing in sin's dark val-ley; No hope with-in could I
2. He left the Fa-ther with all His rich-es, With calmness sweet and se-
3. Death's chilly wa-ters I'll soon be cross-ing; His hand will lead me safe

see. They searched thru Heaven and found a Sav-ior To save a
rene; Came down from Heav-en and gave His life-blood To make the
o'er. I'll join the cho-rus in that great cit-y, And sing up

CHORUS

poor lost soul like me.
vil-est sin-ner clean. Oh, what a Sav-ior! Oh, hal-le-
there for-ev-er-more.

lu-jah! His heart was bro-ken on Cal-va-ry. His hands were

nail-scarred; His side was riv-en. He gave His life-blood for e-ven me.

When the Savior Reached Down for Me 66

G. E. W.

G. E. Wright

1. Once my soul was a-stray from the Heav -en - ly way, And was wretch-ed and
2. I was near to de-spair when He came to me there, And He showed me that
3. How my heart does rejoice when I hear His sweet voice In the temp-est to

vile as could be; But my Sav - ior in love gave me peace from a-bove,
I could be free; Then He lift - ed my feet, gave me glad-ness complete,
Him I then flee; There to lean on His arm, safe, se-cure from all harm,

CHORUS

1-2 When He reached down His hand for me. When my Sav - ior reached down for
3 Since He for me.

me, When my Sav - ior reached down for me; I was lost and un-
for me, for me;

done, with-out God or His Son, When my Sav - ior reached down for me.
for me.

67 When the Roll Is Called Up Yonder

J. M. B.

James M. Black

1. When the trumpet of the Lord shall sound, and time shall be no more, And the
2. On that bright and cloudless morning when the dead in Christ shall rise, And the
3. Let us la-bor for the Mas-ter from the dawn till set-ting sun, Let us

morn-ing breaks e-ter-nal, bright and fair; When the saved of earth shall gather o-ver
glo-ry of His res-ur-rec-tion share, When His chosen ones shall gather to their
talk of all His wondrous love and care, Then when all of life is o-ver and our

FINE **CHORUS**

on the oth-er shore,
home beyond the skies, And the roll is called up yonder, I'll be there.   When the
work on earth is done,

roll   is called up yon - der, When the roll   is called up
When the roll is called up yonder, I'll be there,   When the roll is called up

D.S.

yon - der, When the roll   is called up yonder, When the
yonder, I'll be there,   When the roll

Love Is Why

W. F. (Bill) Lakey
V. B. (Vep) Ellis

David Ellis
V. B. (Vep) Ellis

68

1. He nev-er said I'd have sil-ver or gold, Yet He has prom-ised me
2. I was a-stray full of sin with its shame, There was no peace with-in,
3. Tho' I have none of this world's precious goods, Yet I'm an heir to all

rich-es un-told; He nev-er suffered a life with-out care, Yet He re-
I was to blame; Tho' un-de-serv-ing, My life so de-filed, Now to my
Heav-en af-fords; Tho' I may nev-er a-chieve earth-ly fame, Yet all of

CHORUS

lieves ev'-ry bur-den I bear.
God I have been rec-on-ciled. Sin stained the Cross with the blood of my Lord,
Heav-en can call me by name.

Yet He per-mit-ted it with-out a word; Why, tell me why He re-

Rit. . . . .

deemed you and me? Love is why you and I are free.

69 Ten Thousand Years

E. C.

Elmer Cole

1. Soon I'll come to the end of my jour-ney, And I'll meet the
2. We will just be-gin to sing love's sweet sto-ry, It's a song

one who gave His life for me; I will thank Him for the love
that the an-gels can-not sing; "I'm re-deemed by the blood

that He gave me, And ten thou-sand years or more I'll reign with
of the Sav-ior", And ten thou-sand years or more I'll praise His

CHORUS

Him. Ten thousand years we'll just be started, ten thou- sand
name.

years we've just be-gun; The bat-tle's o-ver and the

vic-t'ry's been won_____ ten thou-sand years_ and we've just be - gun. _

Take Time to Be Holy

70

William D. Longstaff

George C. Stebbins

1. Take time to be ho - ly, Speak oft with Thy Lord;
2. Take time to be ho - ly, The world rush - es on;
3. Take time to be ho - ly, Let Him be Thy guide,
4. Take time to be ho - ly, Be calm in Thy soul;

A - bide in Him al - ways, And feed on His Word.
Spend much time in se - cret With Je - sus a - lone.
And run not be - fore Him, What - ev - er be - tide.
Each tho't and each mo - tive Be - neath His con - trol.

Make friends of God's chil - dren, Help those who are weak,
By look - ing to Je - sus, Like Him thou shalt be;
In joy or in sor - row Still fol - low the Lord,
Thus led by His Spir - it To foun - tains of love,

For - get - ting in noth - ing His bless-ings to seek.
Thy friends in thy con - duct His like-ness shall see.
And, look - ing to Je - sus, Still trust in His Word.
Thou soon shalt be fit - ted For serv - ice a - bove.

71 Jesus Will Outshine Them All

G. J.

Gordon Jensen

Man-sions will glis-ten on the Hills of Glo - ry, Happy re-unions on streets of gold, An-gel choirs singing— glad prais-es for- ev - er But

Ah

Je-sus will outshine them all!—

1. Oh,— what glory— a-waits me—
2. The sparkling riv er— is flow-ing,.

— in Heav-en's— bright cit-y,—When I get there such sights I'll be-
Hap-py fac- es— all glow-ing, Land of splen dor— where night nev - er

hold!— A mil- lion scenes of rare beau ty will de-mand that I
falls,— The gold- en glass gives re- flection to that cit - ty's per-

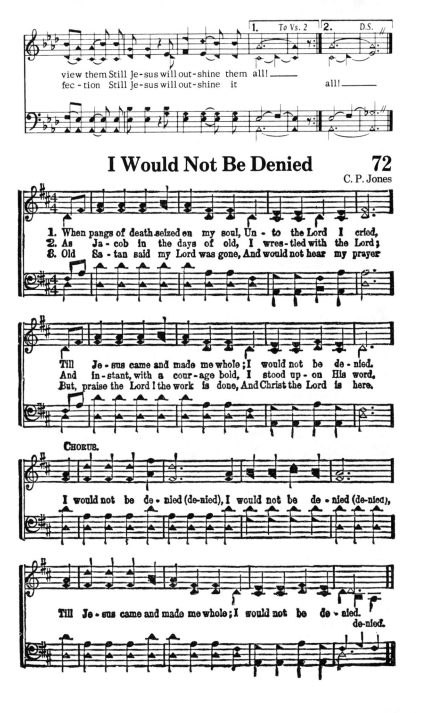

view them Still Je-sus will out-shine them all! _____
fec - tion Still Je-sus will out-shine it   all! _____

I Would Not Be Denied   72

C. P. Jones

1. When pangs of death seized on my soul, Un - to the Lord I cried,
2. As Ja - cob in the days of old, I wres-tled with the Lord;
3. Old Sa - tan said my Lord was gone, And would not hear my prayer

Till Je-sus came and made me whole; I would not be de - nied.
And in-stant, with a cour-age bold, I stood up - on His word.
But, praise the Lord! the work is done, And Christ the Lord is here.

CHORUS.

I would not be de - nied (de-nied), I would not be de - nied (de-nied),

Till Je - sus came and made me whole; I would not be de - nied.
de-nied.

73 Meet Me There

H. E. Blair

Wm. J. Kirkpatrick
Arranged by John T. Benson, Jr.

1. On the happy, golden shore, Where the faithful part no more, When the storms of
2. Here our fond-est hopes are vain, Dearest links are rent in twain; But in heav'n no
3. Where the harps of an-gels ring, And the blest for-ev-er sing, In the pal-ace

life are o'er, Meet me there; Where the night dissolves a-way In-to pure and
throb of pain, Meet me there; By the riv-er sparkling bright In the cit-y
of the King, Meet me there; Where in sweet communion blend Heart with heart and

CHORUS

per-fect day, I am go-ing home to stay, Meet me there.
of de-light, Where our faith is lost in sight, Meet me there. Meet me
friend with friend, In a world that ne'er shall end, Meet me there.

there, Meet me there, Where the tree of life is
Meet me there, Meet me there,

bloom-ing, Meet me there; When the storms of life are o'er, On the
Meet me there;

Arr. © Copyright 1958 in "New Songs of Inspiration No. 3" by John T. Benson, Jr.
International copyright secured. All rights reserved.

hap-py, golden shore, Where the faithful part no more, Meet me there.

Meet me there.

No, Not One 74

Johnson Oatman, Jr.

George C. Hugg

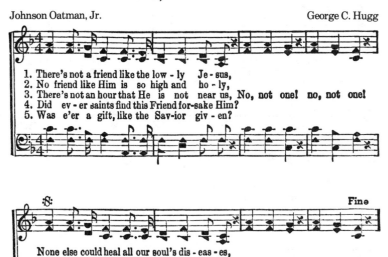

1. There's not a friend like the low - ly Je - sus,
2. No friend like Him is so high and ho - ly,
3. There's not an hour that He is not near us, No, not one! no, not one!
4. Did ev - er saints find this Friend for-sake Him?
5. Was e'er a gift, like the Sav-ior giv - en?

None else could heal all our soul's dis - eas - es,
And yet no friend is so meek and low - ly,
No night so dark but His love can cheer us, No, not one, no, not one!
Or sin - ner find that He would not take him?
Will He re - fuse us a home in heav - en?

D.S.—There's not a friend like the low-ly Je - sus, No, not one, no, not one!

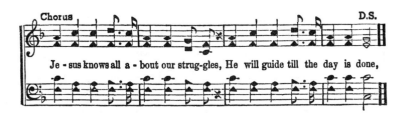

Je - sus knows all a - bout our strug-gles, He will guide till the day is done,

75 Ten Thousand Angels

R. O.

Ray Overholt

mp *Slowly, with much feeling*

1. They bound the hands of Je-sus in the gar-den where He prayed; They
2. Up - on His pre-cious head they placed a crown of thorns; They
3. When they nailed Him to the Cross, His moth-er stood near-by; He
4. To the howl-ing mob He yield-ed; He did not for mer-cy cry. The

led Him thro the streets in shame. They spat up-on the Sav-ior, so
laughed and said, "Be-hold the King." They struck Him and they cursed Him and
said, "Wo-man, be-hold thy son!" He cried, "I thirst for wa-ter," but they
Cross of shame He took a - lone. And when He cried, "It's finished," He

pure and free from sin; They said, "Cru-ci-fy Him; He's to blame."
mocked His ho-ly name. All a - lone He suf-fered ev - 'ry-thing.
gave Him none to drink. Then the sin-ful work of man was done.
gave Him-self to die; Sal - va-tion's wondrous plan was done.

CHORUS *Faster*

He could have called ten thousand an - gels To de-stroy the

world and set Him free. He could have called
the world

ten thou-sand an - gels, But He died a - lone, for you and me.

a - lone

All Hail the Power 76

Edward Perronet

Oliver Holden

1. All hail the pow'r of Je - sus' name! Let an - gels pros - trate fall!
2. Ye cho - sen seed of Is - rael's race, Ye ran - somed from the fall!
3. Let ev - 'ry kin - dred, ev - 'ry tribe, On this ter - res - trial ball,
4. O that with yon - der sa - cred throng We at His feet may fall!

Bring forth the roy - al di - a - dem,
Hail Him who saves you by His grace,
To Him all maj - es - ty as - cribe,
We'll join the ev - er - last - ing song,

And crown Him Lord of all!

Bring forth the roy - al di - a - dem,
Hail Him who saves you by His grace,
To Him all maj - es - ty as - cribe,
We'll join the ev - er - last - ing song,

And crown Him Lord of all!

77 Redemption Draweth Nigh

G. J.

Gordon Jensen

1. Years of time have come and gone since I first heard it told, How Je-
2. Wars and strife on ev - 'ry hand, and vio - lence fills our land, Still some

sus would come a - gain some day; If back then it seemed so real,
peo - ple doubt He'll come a - gain; But the word of God is true,

then I just can't help but feel How much clos - er His com - ing is
He'll re - deem His chos - en few, Don't lose hope, soon Christ Je - sus will

CHORUS

to - day. Signs of the times are ev - 'ry-where. And there's a
de - scend.

brand-new feel - ing in the air; Keep your eyes up - on the

east-ern sky, Lift up your head, re-demp-tion draw-eth nigh.

Hiding in Thee

78

Rev. William O. Cushing

Ira D. Sankey

1. O safe to the Rock that is high - er than I, My soul in its
2. In calm of the noon-tide, in sor - row's lone hour, In times when temp-
3. How oft in the con - flict, when pressed by the foe, I've fled to my

con-flicts and sor - rows would fly; So sin - ful, so wea - ry, Thine, Thine
ta - tions cast o'er me its pow'r; In tem - pest of life, on its wide
Ref - uge and breathed out my woe; How oft - en, when tri - als like sea-

Chorus

would I be; Thou blest Rock of A - ges, I'm hid - ing in Thee.
heav-ing sea, Thou blest Rock of A - ges, I'm hid - ing in Thee. Hid-ing in
bil - lows roll, I've hid - den in Thee, O Thou Rock of my soul.

Thee, Hid - ing in Thee, Thou blest Rock of A - ges, I'm hid - ing in Thee.

79 Through it All

A. C.

Andraé Crouch

1. I've had man-y tears and sor-rows, I've had ques-tions
2. I've been to lots of plac-es, And I've seen a
3. I thank God for the moun-tains And I thank Him

for to-mor-row, There-'ve been times I did-n't know right from
lot of fac-es, There-'ve been times I felt so all a-
for the val-leys, I thank Him for the storms He brought me

wrong. But in ev-'ry sit-u-a-tion, God gave
lone. But in my lone-ly hou-rs, yes, those
through. For if I'd nev-er had a prob-lem, I

bless-ed con-so-la-tion that my tri-als came to
pre-cious lone-ly hou-rs Je-sus let me know that
would-n't know that He could solve them, I'd nev-er know what

CHORUS

on-ly make me strong.
I was His own. Through it all,
faith in God could do.

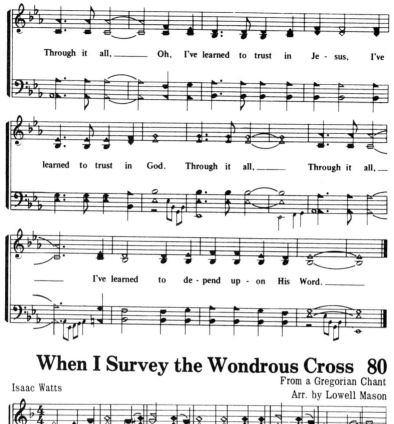

Through it all, _____ Oh, I've learned to trust in Je - sus, I've

learned to trust in God. Through it all, _____ Through it all, _

_____ I've learned to de - pend up - on His Word. _____

When I Survey the Wondrous Cross 80

Isaac Watts

From a Gregorian Chant
Arr. by Lowell Mason

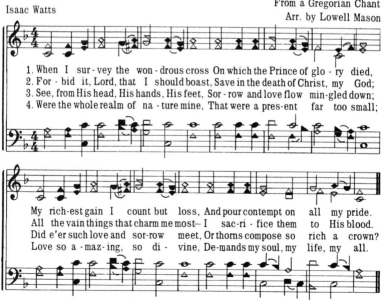

1. When I sur - vey the won - drous cross On which the Prince of glo - ry died,
2. For - bid it, Lord, that I should boast, Save in the death of Christ, my God;
3. See, from His head, His hands, His feet, Sor - row and love flow min - gled down;
4. Were the whole realm of na - ture mine, That were a pres - ent far too small;

My rich - est gain I count but loss, And pour contempt on all my pride.
All the vain things that charm me most— I sac - ri - fice them to His blood.
Did e'er such love and sor - row meet, Or thorns compose so rich a crown?
Love so a - maz - ing, so di - vine, De - mands my soul, my life, my all.

81 I Will Glory in the Cross

D. R.

Dottie Rambo

1. I boast not of works Nor tell of good deeds For
2. My tro - phies and crowns, My robe stained with sin, 'Twas

naught have I done to mer - it His grace, All
all that I had to lay at His feet, Un -

glo - ry and praise shall rest up - on Him, So
wor - thy to eat from the ta - ble of Life 'Til

will - ing to die in my place.
love made pro - vi - sion for me.

CHORUS

I will glo - ry in the cross, in the cross, Lest His

suf-f'ring all be in vain._____ I will weep no more for the

cross that He bore; I will glo - ry in the cross._____

Jesus Paid it All

82

Elvina M. Hall

John T. Grape

1. I hear the Sav-ior say, "Thy strength indeed is small! Child of weakness,
2. Lord, now in-deed I find Thy pow'r, and Thine alone, Can change the
3. For noth-ing good have I Where-by Thy grace to claim—I'll wash my
4. And when be-fore the throne I stand in Him complete, "Jesus died my

watch and pray, Find in Me thine all in all."
lep-er's spots And melt the heart of stone.
garments white In the blood of Cal-v'ry's Lamb.
soul to save," My lips shall still re-peat.

Jesus paid it all, All to

Him I owe; Sin had left a crim-son stain—He washed it white as snow.

83   Nailing My Sins to His Cross

W. E. M.   W. Elmo Mercer

1. That day when they cru-ci-fied my Sav-ior ___ He was
2. Al-though this was cen-tur-ies a-go now ___ And I

will-ing ___ to pay ___ all the cost ___ When they drove
was-n't e-ven liv-ing then at all ___ The Bi-ble

nails. cru-el nails through His bod-y ___ They were nail-ing
says Je-sus died for all sin-ners ___ This in-cludes me

CHORUS

my sins to His cross ___ O the shame of it! My sins
O praise His dear name! ___

cru-ci-fied Him that day! My sins were to blame ___ For-give.

Lord, I pray! I'll live so the world can know I love Him

For nail-ing my sins to His cross!   cross
to His cross!

_1_ D.C. _2_ FINE

Only Trust Him

84

J. H. S.   John H. Stockton

1. Come, ev-'ry soul by sin op-pressed—There's mer-cy with the Lord,
2. For Je-sus shed His pre-cious blood, Rich bless-ings to be-stow;
3. Yes, Je-sus is the Truth, the Way, That leads you in-to rest;

And He will sure-ly give you rest By trust-ing in His word.
Plunge now in-to the crim-son flood That wash-es white as snow.
Be-lieve in Him with-out de-lay And you are ful-ly blest.

CHORUS   1.   2

On-ly trust Him, on-ly trust Him, On-ly trust Him now;
He will save you, He will save you, He will save you now.

85 Hide Thou Me

L. R. Tolbert

Thoro Harris

1. Some-times I feel dis-cour-aged, and think my life in vain,
2. Some-times it seems I dare not go one step far-ther on,
3. O what a Friend is Je - sus, sure An-chor for my soul,

I'm tempt-ed then to mur-mur, and of my lot com-plain;
And from my heart all cour-age has dis - ap-peared and gone;
So ten - der, true and gra-cious, I'm safe in His con - trol.

But when I think of Je - sus, and all He's done for me.
But, I re-mem - ber Je - sus, and all His love for me.
My help in time of dan - ger, my strong de-fense is He.

Then, I cry, O Rock of A - ges, Hide Thou me.
Then, I cry, O Rock of A - ges, Hide Thou me.
O Thou bless - ed Rock of A - ges, Hide Thou me.

Chorus

O Rock of A - ges, Hide Thou me, No oth-er Ref - uge,

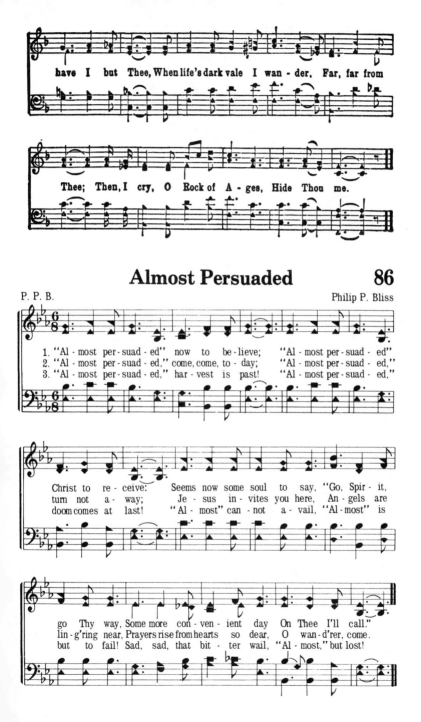

have I but Thee, When life's dark vale I wan - der, Far, far from

Thee; Then, I cry, O Rock of A - ges, Hide Thou me.

Almost Persuaded 86

P. P. B.

Philip P. Bliss

1. "Al - most per - suad - ed" now to be - lieve; "Al - most per - suad - ed"
2. "Al - most per - suad - ed," come, come, to - day; "Al - most per - suad - ed,"
3. "Al - most per - suad - ed," har - vest is past! "Al - most per - suad - ed,"

Christ to re - ceive: Seems now some soul to say, "Go, Spir - it,
turn not a - way; Je - sus in - vites you here, An - gels are
doom comes at last! "Al - most" can - not a - vail, "Al - most" is

go Thy way, Some more con - ven - ient day On Thee I'll call."
lin - g'ring near, Prayers rise from hearts so dear, O wan - d'rer, come.
but to fail! Sad, sad, that bit - ter wail, "Al - most," but lost!

87 Tears Will Never Stain the Streets of That City

D. R.

Dottie Rambo

1. If I could count the tears that have fal - en,
2. I've nev - er met one man with - out sor - row,
3. I have ques - tioned the loss of a loved one,

It would seem like an o - cean to me; And if my
Nev - er looked in - to eyes with no pain; But there's a
The grave seems so fi - nal and cold; But we'll

heart were a win - dow you could look through,
land where grief is a stran - ger, And
meet a - gain where death has no vic - t'ry, In a

CHORUS:

Oh the pain and scars you would see. But
joy is the on - ly song they sing. And tears will
land where we'll ne - ver grow old. And

nev - er stain the streets of that ci - ty, No wreaths of death on

my man-sion door;___ Tear-drops aren't welcome be-yond the gates of

glo-ry,___ 'Cause the heart will nev-er break ___ an - y - more. ___

What a Friend
88

Joseph Scriven

C. C. Converse

1. What a Friend we have in Je - sus, All our sins and griefs to bear!
2. Have we tri - als and temp - ta - tions? Is there trou-ble an - y - where?
3. Are we weak and heav - y la - den, Cumbered with a load of care?

What a priv - i - lege to car - ry Ev - 'ry-thing to God in pray'r!
We should nev - er be dis - cour-aged, Take it to the Lord in pray'r.
Pre-cious Sav - ior, still our ref - uge, Take it to the Lord in pray'r.

D S.-All be-cause we do not car - ry Ev - 'ry-thing to God in pray'r.
Je - sus knows our ev - 'ry weak-ness, Take it to the Lord in pray'r.
In His arms He'll take and shield thee, Thou wilt find a sol - ace there.

O what peace we oft - en for - feit, O what need-less pain we bear,
Can we find a friend so faith-ful, Who will all our sor-rows share?
Do thy friends despise, for-sake thee? Take it to the Lord in prayer;

89 Surely Goodness and Mercy

John W. Peterson
Alfred B. Smith

J. W. P. & A. B. S.

1. A pil-grim was I and a-wand'ring, In the cold night of sin I did roam; When Je-sus the kind Shepherd found me, And now I am on my way home.
2. He re-stor-eth my soul when I'm wea-ry, He giv-eth me strength day by day; He leads me be-side the still wa-ters, He guards me each step of the way.
3. When I walk thru that dark lonesome val-ley, My Sav-ior will walk with me there; And safe-ly His great hand will lead me To the man-sions He's gone to pre-pare.

CHORUS

Sure-ly good-ness and mer-cy shall fol-low me All the days, all the days of my life,.............. Sure-ly good-ness and mer-cy shall fol-low me All the days, all the days

Fine (opt. CODA)

of my life. And I shall dwell in the house of the Lord for-ev-er,

And I will feast at the ta-ble spred for me.   Sure-ly

D. S. al Fine

Have Thine Own Way, Lord 90

Adelaide A. Pollard   Geo. C. Stebbins

1. Have Thine own way, Lord! Have Thine own way!   Thou art the
2. Have Thine own way, Lord! Have Thine own way!   Search me and
3. Have Thine own way, Lord! Have Thine own way!   Wound-ed and
4. Have Thine own way, Lord! Have Thine own way!   Hold o'er my

Pot-ter, I am the clay.   Mold me and make me
try me, Mas-ter, to-day!   Whit-er than snow, Lord,
wea-ry, Help me, I pray!   Pow-er, all pow-er,
be-ing, Ab-so-lute sway!   Fill with Thy Spir-it

Aft-er Thy will,   While I am wait-ing,   Yielded and still.
Wash me just now,   As in Thy pres-ence   Hum-bly I bow.
Sure-ly is Thine!   Touch me and heal me,   Sav-ior di-vine!
Till all shall see   Christ on-ly, al-ways,   Liv-ing in me!

91 A Song Holy Angels Cannot Sing

G. J.

Gordon Jensen

1. An-gels nev - er knew the joy ___ that is mine, ___ For the
2. ___ "Ho - ly is the Lord," the an - gels sing, ___ ___ Be -

blood has nev - er washed their sins a - way; ___ ___ Tho' they sing in
fore the throne of God con - tin - ual - ly; ___ For me to join their

Heav - en there will come a time ___ ___ When si - lent - ly they'll
song will be a nat - 'ral thing, ___ But they just won't know the

CHORUS:

lis - ten to me sing "A - maz - ing Grace." ___ And it's a
words ___ ___ to "Love ___ Lift - ed Me." ___

song ho - ly an - gels can - not sing, ___ "A - maz - ing Grace, ___

How sweet the sound!"____ It's a song ho - ly an - gels can - not

sing, ____ "I once was lost,_____ but now I'm found."____

Where the Roses Never Fade   92

E., J., & J.   Elsie, Jack, and Jim

1. I am go - ing to a cit - y Where the streets with gold are laid,
2. In this world we have our trou - bles, Sa - tan's snares we must e - vade;
3. Loved ones gone to be with Je - sus, In their robes of white ar - rayed.

Where the tree of life is bloom - ing, And the ros - es nev - er fade.
We'll be free from all temp - ta - tions Where the ros - es nev - er fade.
Now are wait - ing for my com - ing Where the ros - es nev - er fade.

D. S.-I am go - ing to a cit - y Where the ros - es nev - er fade.
CHORUS

Here they bloom but for a sea - son, Soon their beau - ty is de - cayed;

93 What Sins Are You Talkin' About?

H. L. and B. L. S.

Harold Lane and Ben L. Speer

1. I re-mem-ber the days when I was bent low With the bur-den of sin ___ and strife, ___ Then Je-sus came in and res-cued me, and He gave me a brand new life; ___ And now as I thank Him day af-ter day for ___ wash-ing my sins ___ a-way, ___ It

2. When my flesh be-comes weak it's then I can speak to the Sav-ior Who's with me each day, ___ "Oh, Fa-ther, for-give me, Hear my plea," and He wash-es my sin a-way; ___ Each time that I bow to give ___ Him thanks for re-mov-ing my guilt ___ and shame, ___ He

seems I can al - most ___ hear ___ the voice of the
can - not re - call what I'm talk - in' a - bout, For His

CHORUS

Bless - ed Sav - ior say:
an - swer is al - ways the same. "What sins are you

talk - in' a - bout, I don't re - mem - ber them an - y

more; ___ From the Book of Life they've all been torn

out, I don't re - mem - ber them an - y more." ___

94   I Stand Upon the Rock of Ages

S. P., Jr.

Squire Parsons, Jr.

1. When the an - gry winds are blow - ing and the storm is
2. This ____ rock is Christ, my Sav - ior, my ____ soul He

all a - round; Oh, how sweet it is in know - ing that a
will de - fend; Trust - ing dai - ly in His fa - vor, on His

CHORUS

ref - uge I have found.   Stand up - on, stand up - on the
prom - ise I de - pend.   I stand up - on

bless - ed, ho - ly ____ Rock of A - ges, And safe with -
safe

in, safe with - in His shel - ter I will be; The
with - in

Winds may blow, winds may blow and the an - gry
winds may blow

storm all a - round me rag - es, On the Rock,
Up - on the

sol - id Rock of A - ges I shall be.
Rock

O for a Thousand Tongues to Sing 95

Charles Wesley

Carl G. Glaser
Arr. by Lowell Mason

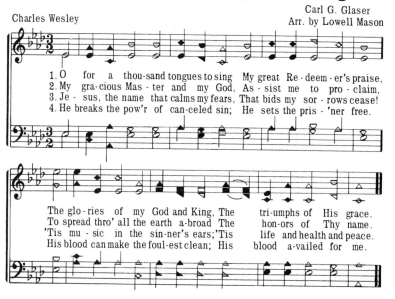

1. O for a thou-sand tongues to sing My great Re - deem - er's praise,
2. My gra - cious Mas - ter and my God, As - sist me to pro - claim,
3. Je - sus, the name that calms my fears, That bids my sor - rows cease!
4. He breaks the pow'r of can-celed sin; He sets the pris - 'ner free.

The glo - ries of my God and King, The tri - umphs of His grace.
To spread thro' all the earth a-broad The hon - ors of Thy name.
'Tis mu - sic in the sin-ner's ears; 'Tis life and health and peace.
His blood can make the foul-est clean; His blood a-vailed for me.

96 Showing My Appreciation

J. H.

Joel Hemphill

1. ___ Christ, the Sav - ior died ___ for sin - ners on ___ the cross on a hill called Cal - va - ry; He beck - ons to those who are hea - vy la - den, "Who - so - ev - er will" in - clud - ed me! ___

2. When He as - cend - ed He left the prom - ise that He'd pre - pare us a home e - ter - nal - ly; ___ Now my soul has an - ti - ci - pa - tion, But while I'm wait - ing there is vic - to - ry! ___

CHORUS

Show - ing my ap - pre - ci -

a - tion in the on - ly ways that I can, _____

By my liv - ing, and my giv - ing,

and by lov - ing my fel - low - man. _____

I Am Bound for the Promised Land 97

Samuel Stennett

American melody
Arr. R. M. McIntosh

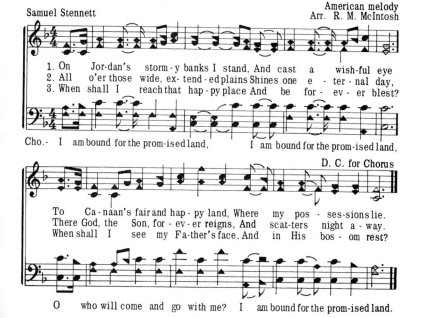

1. On Jor-dan's storm-y banks I stand, And cast a wish-ful eye
2. All o'er those wide, ex - tend - ed plains Shines one e - ter - nal day,
3. When shall I reach that hap - py place And be for - ev - er blest?

Cho.- I am bound for the prom-ised land, I am bound for the prom-ised land,

D. C. for Chorus

To Ca-naan's fair and hap - py land, Where my pos - ses-sions lie.
There God, the Son, for - ev - er reigns, And scat-ters night a - way.
When shall I see my Fa-ther's face, And in His bos - om rest?

O who will come and go with me? I am bound for the prom-ised land.

98 Innocent Blood

G. J.

Gordon Jensen

1. On - ly one Man, _____ has ev - er been known, ___
2. Nails forged by hands _____ guil - ty of crime, ___

in this world, _____ to live a - bove sin. _____
pierced the on - ly hands that were clean. _____

(Cue notes for verse 2)

Yet this in - no - cent Man with His own pre - cious Blood,
_____ Love far be - yond mor - tal love ____ al - lowed;

paid the price, My guil - ty soul's par - don to win. ___
For my sake, the shame heaped on Heav - en's King. ___

CHORUS

In - no - cent blood _____ was spilled for ____ me;

Innocent blood shed at Calvary.

When Jesus died on the Cross, long ago:

Innocent blood bought my soul.

O Master, Let Me Walk with Thee 99

Washington Gladden   H. Percy Smith

1. O Master, let me walk with Thee In lowly paths of service free;
2. Help me the slow of heart to move By some clear, winning word of love;
3. Teach me Thy patience! still with Thee In closer, dearer company,
4. In hope that sends a shining ray Far down the future's broad'ning way,

Tell me Thy secret–help me bear The strain of toil, the fret of care.
Teach me the wayward feet to stay And guide them in the homeward way.
In work that keeps faith sweet and strong, In trust that triumphs over wrong.
In peace that only Thou canst give, With Thee, O Master, let me live.

100 (Jesus Will Be What Makes it) Heaven for Me

L. W.

Lanny Wolfe

1. I've heard of a land that is won-drous-ly fair, ____ They
2. If walls there weren't jas-per, if streets were not gold, ____ If

say that it's splen-dor is far be-yond com-pare; ____ In that
man-sions would crum-ble, if folks ____ there grew old; ____ Still I'd

place that's called Heav - en my ____ soul longs to be, ____ For
see ev - 'ry - thing, ____ I've been long-ing to see, ____ If

where Je - sus is, ____ It will be Heav-en for me.
Je - sus is there, ____ It will be Heav-en for me.

CHORUS:

Heav - en for me, Heav - en for me, Je - sus will

be what makes it Heav-en for me;____ All its beau-ty and

won-ders I'm long-ing to see,____ But Je-sus will

be ____ what makes it Heav-en for me.

Must Jesus Bear the Cross Alone 101

Thomas Shepherd

George N. Allen

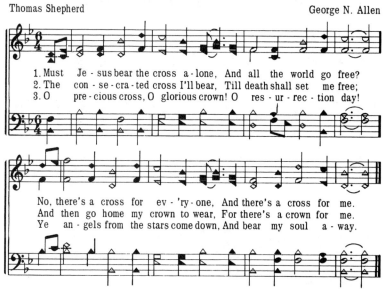

1. Must Je-sus bear the cross a-lone, And all the world go free?
2. The con-se-cra-ted cross I'll bear, Till death shall set me free;
3. O pre-cious cross, O glorious crown! O res-ur-rec-tion day!

No, there's a cross for ev-'ry-one, And there's a cross for me.
And then go home my crown to wear, For there's a crown for me.
Ye an-gels from the stars come down, And bear my soul a-way.

102 He Looked Beyond My Fault (And Saw My Need)

Lyrics by
Dottie Rambo
Intro.

Adapted from Londonderry Aire

A - maz - ing grace shall al - ways be my song of praise, For it was grace that bought my lib - er - ty; I do not know just why He came to love me so, He looked be - yond my fault, and saw my need. I shall for - ev - er lift mine eyes to Cal - va - ry, To view the

cross where Je - sus died for me; How mar - vel-

ous the grace that caught my fall - ing soul, He

looked be - yond my fault and saw my need.

Hear Our Prayer, O Lord 103

George Whelpton

Hear our prayer, O Lord, Hear our prayer, O Lord;

In-cline Thine ear to us, And grant us Thy peace. A - men.

104 Only Jesus Can Satisfy Your Soul

L.W.

Lanny Wolfe

1. The world will try to sat - is - fy ___ that ___ long - ing in your
2. If you could have the fame and for-tune, all the wealth you could ob-

soul, You may search the wide world o'er, ___ but you'll be just as be-
tain, Yet you have not Christ with - in, your liv - ing here would be in

fore! You'll nev - er find true sat - is - fac-tion ___ un - til you've
vain: There'll come a time when death shall call you, ___ rich - es can-not

found the Lord, For on - ly Je - sus ___ ___ can sat - is - fy your soul.
help you then, So come to Je - sus ___ for on-ly He can sat - is - fy.

CHORUS

Sat-is-fy your soul, on-ly Je-sus ___ can sat-is-fy your soul, _____
soul, sat-is-fy your

soul. And on-ly He — can change your heart and make you whole:

He'll give you peace — you nev-er knew, — (sweet) love and joy —

and heav-en, too, For on-ly Je-sus — can sat-is-fy your soul! —

Jesus Loves Even Me   105

P. P. B.

P. P. Bliss

1. { I am so glad that our Father in heav'n Tells of His love in the Book He has giv'n;
Won-der-ful things in the Bi-ble I see, This is the dearest, that Jesus loves me.

2. { Tho   I forget Him and wander away, Still He doth love me wher-ev-er I stray;
Back to His dear loving arms would I flee, When I remember that Jesus loves me.

3. { O   there is on-ly one song I can sing, When in His beauty I see the great King;
This shall my song in e - ter-ni-ty be, "O what a wonder that Jesus loves me."

Chorus

I am so glad that Jesus loves me, Jesus loves me, Jesus loves me,   e-ven me.

106 I See Jesus

C. B. W.

Charles B. Wycuff

1. Once a man named Ste - phen, preached a - bout the Lord,
2. As the stones fell on him, beat - ing out his life,
3. Thro' the gates of glo - ry, down the streets of gold,

Folks were saved and folks were healed, As they heard his word;
Ste - phen knew he'd soon be thro', with all toil and strife;
Marched a he - ro of the Lord, In - to heav - ens fold;

Sa - tan did not like it, soon he had his crowd,
So much like the mas - ter, with a heart so true,
When he met the Sav - ior, at the great white throne,

And as he was tried they heard Ste - phen cry a - loud.
He prayed "Lord for - give for they know not what they do"
I be - lieve He smiled and said, "Ste - phen wel - come home"

CHORUS

"I see Je - sus, stand - ing at the Fa - ther's right hand,

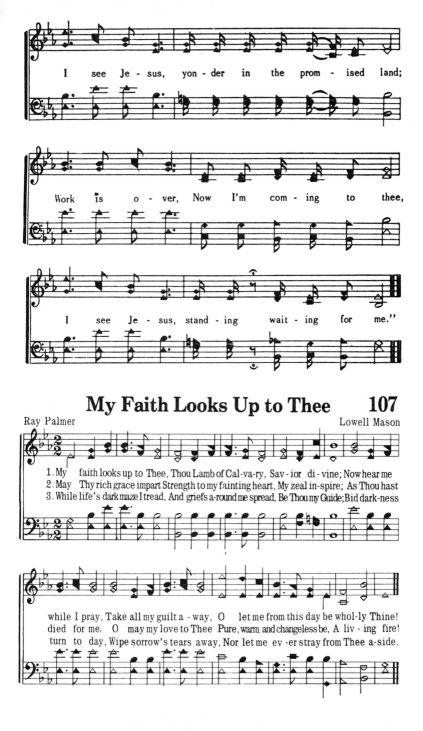

I see Jesus, yon-der in the prom-ised land;

Work is o-ver, Now I'm com-ing to thee,

I see Je-sus, stand-ing wait-ing for me."

My Faith Looks Up to Thee 107

Ray Palmer

Lowell Mason

1. My faith looks up to Thee, Thou Lamb of Cal-va-ry, Sav-ior di-vine; Now hear me
2. May Thy rich grace impart Strength to my fainting heart, My zeal in-spire; As Thou hast
3. While life's dark maze I tread, And griefs a-round me spread, Be Thou my Guide; Bid dark-ness

while I pray, Take all my guilt a-way, O let me from this day be whol-ly Thine!
died for me, O may my love to Thee Pure, warm, and changeless be, A liv-ing fire!
turn to day, Wipe sorrow's tears away, Nor let me ev-er stray from Thee a-side.

108 I Learned About Jesus
(in Grandma's Rocking Chair)

J. H.

Joel Hemphill

1. I went to live with Grand-ma____ when I was just a
2. I used to love to hear her hum as she worked through the

kid, And if some-one____ ev-er need-ed some-one,
day, ____ And each night at____ bed-time____ I

I'm some-one who did; She loved Grand-pa and
loved to hear her pray; She told me a-bout

Je-sus with plen-ty love to share, And she told me all a-
heav-en ____ wait-ing 'way up there, And____ I first felt the

bout it in that big old rock-ing chair.
feel-ing in my grand-ma's rock-ing chair.

CHORUS

I learned a-bout Je - sus in grand-ma's rock - ing chair, And some-times when I'm trou - bled I wish that I were there; For when she sang of His sweet love, I did-n't have a care, I learned a-bout Je - sus in my grand-ma's rock - ing chair.

109 Holy Spirit, Thou Art Welcome

D. R.

Dottie Rambo and David Huntsinger
Arr. by W. Elmo Mercer

1. Holy Spir - it, Thou art wel - come
2. Ho - ly Spir - it, Thou art wel - come

in this place; Holy Spir - it, Thou art
in this place; Ho - ly Spir - it, Thou art

wel - come in this place; Om -
wel - come in this place; Om -

nip - o - tent Fa - ther of mer - cy and
nip - o - tent Fa - ther of mer - cy and

grace! Thou art wel - come in _____ this
grace! Thou art wel - come in _____ this

CHORUS

place. _____ Lord, in Thy pres - ence there's
place. _____ Fill all the hun - gry and

heal - ing di - vine; ___ No oth - er pow - er
emp - ty with - in; Re - store us, oh Fa - ther,

can save, Lord, but Thine; _____ Ho - ly
re - vive us a - gain; _____ Ho - ly

Spir - it, Thou art wel - come in this place;
Spir - it, Thou art wel - come in this place;

Thou art wel - come in _____ this place.
Thou art wel - come in _____ this place. _____

110 If We Never Meet Again

A. E. B.

Albert E. Brumley

Slow

1. Soon we'll come to the end of life's jour - ney And per-
2. O so oft - en we're part - ed with sor - row, Ben - e-
3. O they say we shall meet by the riv - er, Where no

haps we'll nev - er meet an - y more, Till we gath - er in
dic - tions oft - en quick - en our pain, But we nev - er shall
storm-clouds ev - er dark - en the sky, And they say we'll be

heav-en's bright cit - y Far a - way on that beau - ti - ful shore.
sor - row in heav - en, God be with you till we meet a - gain.
hap - py in heav-en In the won-der - ful sweet by and by.

CHORUS

Nev - er meet this side of heav - en
If we nev - er meet a - gain this side of heav - en

Strug - gle thru this world and its strife,
As we strug-gle thru this world and its strife, There's an-

Meet - ing place   some-where in heav - en   By the
oth - er meet-ing place somewhere in heav - en   By the

By   the shin - ing riv - er of life;   Ros - es bloom
side of the riv - er of life;   Where the charming roses bloom for-

ev - er and ev - er,   Sep - a - ra - tions
ev - er,   And where sep - a - ra - tions come no

come nev - er more   Nev - er   meet
more,   If we nev - er meet a - gain this side of

this side of heav-en   Meet you on that beau-ti-ful shore.
heav-en   I will meet you on that beau-ti-ful shore.

111

I've Got a Reservation

S. P., Jr.

Squire Parsons, Jr.

1. There is a land that I have been told, where the streets are paved with pure gold And the bright flow - ers bloom through all e - ter - ni - ty, (e - ter - ni - ty;) Man - sions are glist - 'ning on the bright shore, beau - ty this world could nev - er af - ford, And I've got a res - er - va - tion, my name's been writ - ten down.

2. There is a ban - quet ta - ble that's spread, filled with milk and hon - ey and bread, Where we shall dine while the e - ter - nal a - ges roll, (while a - ges roll;) Friends and loved ones will be there, robed in gar - ments bright and fair, And I've got a res - er - va - tion, my name's been writ - ten down.

CHORUS

I've got _____ a res-er-va-tion to walk on the streets of gold, I've got _____ a res-er-va-tion where the pearl-y gates un-fold. In heav-en my name's been writ-ten down, I'm long-ing to hear that trum-pet sound, I've got _____ a res-er-va-tion, my name's been writ-ten down.

112
Touring That City

H. L.

Harold Lane

1. Man-y times I have won-dered 'bout the sights of that
2. Here on earth we have trou-bles that to us seem so

cit-y, and___ all that my eyes shall be-hold;___ I will
heav-y, but in Heav-en no one will be sad;___ Mom and

see all the won-ders when I en-ter that cit-y there for-
Dad will be sing-ing, Heav-en's praise will be ring-ing for the

CHORUS:

ev-er to be safe in His fold.___ Some morn-ing you'll
dear-est Friend___ I ev-er had. ___

find me tour-ing that cit-y, where the Son of God is the

Light, ___ You'll find me there on the streets ___ so pret-ty, made of gold ___ so pure and so bright; ___ With Je-sus, the One, Who gave me the vic-t'ry, Who ___ led me a-cross the di-vide, ___ Some morn-ing you'll find me tour-ing that cit-y, where with Him I will ev-er a-bide. ___

113 Wonderful Love

J. D. S.

J. D. Sumner

Won-der-ful love, wonder-ful love down from above down from above
and it means all the world all the world to me. Frees from my sin
frees from my sin, gives peace within sweet peace within
won-der-ful love wonder-ful, marvelous love, God's wonderful love.
I can't explain, ex - plain all the joy, joy that He placed, placed in my heart

Won - der-ful love coming down from a - bove
and it means all the world to me. It frees
from my sin, gives me sweet peace within. Oh, what
won - derful, won - der-ful love. I can't ex -
plain all the joy that He placed in my heart,

giv-ing me   perfect peace   sweet peace for my soul.
giv- ing me   per-fect peace   for my soul.   I'll nev - er

I'll nev - er stray,   stray from His love   un - til I reach
stray   from His love   when I reach   home a -

home up a-bove. Wonderful love, wonderful mar-velous love God's wonderful love.
bove.   Oh, what won - derful, won - der - ful love,

Coda

Wonderful love coming down from above, Peace in my heart that will nev- er depart.
                                                                                                    My

Rit.

Wonder-ful love.

heart over flows for my love for Him grows O what wonderful, wonder-ful love.

114 I'll See You in the Rapture

C. B. F.

Charles B. Feltner

1. If we nev - er meet a - gain on this earth, my pre - cious
2. To my loved ones let me say that there'll sure - ly come a

friend, If, to God, we have been true and we've
day When the Lord will come a - gain and He'll

lived a - bove all sin; Then, for us, there'll be a
take His bride a - way; So, get read - y now to

greet - ing, for there's gon - na be a meet - ing, I'll
meet Him, and with hal - le - lu - jahs greet Him, I'll

see you in the rap - ture some sweet day.

I'll see you in the rap-ture, see you in the rap-ture, See you at that meet-ing in the air; There, with our bless-ed Sav-ior, we'll live and reign for-ev-er, I'll see you in the rap-ture some sweet day.

115 Sound the Battle Cry!

W. F. S.

Wm. F. Sherwin

1. Sound the bat-tle cry! See, the foe is nigh; Raise the standard high For the Lord; Gird your ar-mor on, Stand firm, ev-'ry one; Rest your cause up-on His ho-ly word.

2. Strong to meet the foe, Marching on we go, While our cause we know, Must pre-vail; Shield and banner bright, Gleam-ing in the light; Bat-tling for the right We ne'er can fail.

3. O Thou God of all, Hear us when we call, Help us one and all By Thy grace; When the bat-tle's done, And the vic-t'ry's won, May we wear the crown Be-fore Thy face.

CHORUS ff

Rouse, then, sol-diers, ral-ly round the ban-ner, Read-y, stead-y, pass the word a-long; On-ward, for ward, shout a-loud Ho-san-na! Christ is Cap-tain of the might-y throng.

Supper Time

116

I. F. S.

Ira F. Stanphill

Duet Soprano (or Tenor) and Alto

1. When I was but a boy in days of child-hood I used to play till eve-ning shad-ows come Then wind-ing down an old fa-mil-iar path-way I heard my moth-er call at set of sun.

2. One day be-side her bed-side I was kneel-ing And an-gel wings were win-now-ing the air She heard the call for Sup-per Time in heav-en And now I know she's wait-ing for me there. Come home, come

3. In vi-sions now I see her stand-ing yon-der And her fa-mil-iar voice I hear once more, The ban-quet ta-ble's read-y up in heav-en It's sup-per time up-on the gold-en strand.

CHORUS

Come home, come home it's sup-per time, The shad-ows length-in fast, Come home, come home it's sup-per time; We're go-ing home at last.

O I Want to See Him

R. H. Cornelius
Arr. by R. E. Winsett

R. H. C.

1. As I jour-ney thru the land sing-ing as I go, Point-ing souls to
2. When in serv-ice for my Lord dark may be the night, But I'll cling more
3. When in val-leys low I look t'ward the mountain height, And be-hold my
4. When be-fore me bil-lows rise from the might-y deep, Then my Lord di-

Cal-va-ry, to the crim-son flow, Man-y ar-rows pierce my soul
close to Him, He will give me light; Sa-tan's snares may vex my soul,
Sav-ior there, lead-ing in the fight, With a tender hand outstretched
rects my bark, He doth safe-ly keep, And He leads me gen-tly on

FINE

from with-out, with-in; But my Lord leads me on, thru Him I must win.
turn my tho'ts a-side; But my Lord goes a-head, leads what-e'er be-tide.
t'ward the val-ley low; Guid-ing me, I can see, as I on-ward go.
thru this world be-low; He's a real friend to me, O I love Him so.

D. S.-Cares all past, Home at last, ev-er to re-joice.

CHORUS

O I want to see Him, look up-on His face, There to sing for-ev-er

D. S.

of His sav-ing grace;   On the streets of Glory let me lift my voice;
          His saving grace;

Hallelujah, We Shall Rise

118

Last V. by R. E. W.

Words and Music by J. E. Thomas

Not too fast

1. In the res-ur-rec-tion morn-ing, When the trump of God shall sound,
2. In the res-ur-rec-tion morn-ing, What a meet-ing it will be,
3. In the res-ur-rec-tion morn-ing, Bless-ed tho't it is to me,
4. In the res-ur-rec-tion morn-ing, We shall meet Him in the air,

We shall rise, we shall rise! Then the saints will come re-joic-ing,
When our fa-thers and our moth-ers,
I shall see my bless-ed Sav-ior

Hal-le-lu-jah! And be car-ried up to glo-ry

And no tears will e'er be found, We shall rise, we shall rise!
And our loved ones we shall see,
Who so free-ly died for me,
To our home so bright and fair, Hal-le-lu-jah!

FINE

D. S.-Hal-le-lujah! in that morning we shall rise.

CHORUS

Hal-le-lu-jah! Amen! We shall rise!
We shall rise, we shall rise! Hal-le-lu-jah!

D. S.

In the res-ur-rec-tion morn-ing, When death's pris-on bars are brok-en,

119 Just Over in the Glory Land

Jas. W. Acuff   Emmet S. Dean

1. I've a home pre-pared where the saints a-bide, Just o-ver in the glo-ry land;
2. I am on my way to those mansions fair, Just o-ver in the glo-ry land;
3. What a joy-ful thought that my Lord I'll see, Just o-ver in the glo-ry land;
4. With the blood-washed throng I will shout and sing, Just o-ver in the glo-ry land;

And I long to be by my Sa-vior's side, Just o-ver in the glo-ry land.
There to sing God's praise and His glo-ry share, Just o-ver in the glo-ry land.
And with kindred saved, there for-ev-er be, Just o-ver in the glo-ry land.
Glad ho-san-nas to Christ, the Lord and King, Just o-ver in the glo-ry land.

CHORUS.

Just o - ver in the glo-ry land, I'll join the hap-py
Just o-ver, o-ver   I'll join, yes, join

an-gel band, Just o-ver in the glo-ry land; Just o - ver
                                              Just o-ver, o-ver

in the glo-ry land, There with the might-y host I'll stand,
                     There with, yes, with

Press Along to Gloryland

120

James Rowe

Emmett S. Dean

1. O ransomed souls, with joyous song, Press a-long to Glo-ry-land;
2. The foe may rave, but Christ will save,
3. To join once more those gone before,
4. The crown to wear for - ev - er there, Press along

Ex - tol-ling grace that saves the race, Press along to Glo-ry - land.
The storm may sweep, but He will keep,
With saints to sing be - fore the King,
To sing His praise thru countless days, Press a-long

Chorus

Press a - long, glad soul, press a - long, Giv - ing
Press a - long,

out the mes-sage grand; Let -ting love, God's
Giv-ing out Let -ting love,

love, be your song, Press a - long to Glo - ry - land.
Press a - long

121   A Beautiful Life

W. M. G.

Wm. M. Golden

1. Each day I'll do.............. a gold-en deed, ... By help-ing
2. To be a child.............. of God each day,.............. My light must
3. The on-ly life.............. that will en-dure,.............. Is one that's
4. I'll help some one,.............. in time of need,.............. And jour-ney
5. While go-ing down.............. life's wea-ry road,.............. I'll try to

those..........who are in need;..........My life on earth........is but a
shine..........a-long the way;..........I'll sing His praise........while a-ges
kind..........and good and pure;..........And so for God..........I'll take my
on ....with rap-id speed;..........I'll help the sick..........and poor and
lift..........some trav-ler's load;..........I'll try to turn..........the night to

span,..........And so I'll do............the best I can, the best I can.
roll............And strive to help............some trou-bled soul, some troubled soul.
stand,........Each day I'll lend..........a help-ing hand, a help-ing hand.
weak,..........And words of kind - ness to them speak, kind words I'll speak.
day,.......... Make flow-ers bloom..........a-long the way, the lone-ly way.

CHORUS

Life's evening sun.............. is sink-ing low,.......... A few more days............

and I must go To meet the deeds................ that I have
and I must go..................... To meet the deeds

done,............Where there will be..................... no set-ting sun.....................

that I have done, Where there will be no set-ting sun.

My Jesus, I Love Thee

122

William R. Featherston

A. J. Gordon

1. My Je - sus, I love Thee, I know Thou art mine; For Thee all the
2. I love Thee be-cause Thou hast first lov - ed me, And purchased my
3. I'll love Thee in life, I will love Thee in death, And praise Thee as
4. In man - sions of glo - ry and end - less de - light, I'll ev - er a-

fol - lies of sin I re - sign; My gra - cious Re - deem - er, my
par - don on Cal - va - ry's tree; I love Thee for wear - ing the
long as Thou lend-est me breath, And say when the death - dew lies
dore Thee in Heav-en so bright; I'll sing with the glit - ter - ing

Sav - ior art Thou; If ev - er I loved Thee, my Je - sus, 'tis now.
thorns on Thy brow; If ev - er I loved Thee, my Je - sus, 'tis now.
cold on my brow; "If ev - er I loved Thee, my Je - sus, 'tis now."
crown on my brow; "If ev - er I loved Thee, my Je - sus, 'tis now."

123 Redeemed

James Rowe

S. A Ganus

1. Sweet is the song............ I am sing-ing to - day;......
2. Great is my joy .... now as on -ward I go; ......
3. Pre - cious in - deed........ .... is my Sav - ior to me; ......

.... I'm re - deemed!.... I'm re - deemed!.... Trou-ble and
.... I'm re - deemed!.... I'm re - deemed!.... All the way
.... I'm re - deemed!.... I'm re - deemed!.... Hap-py in

sor - row .... have van-ished a - way;..........
homeward .... my prais-es shall flow;..........
glo - ry............. some day I shall be; .... I have

Chorus

I have been redeemed! I'm re - deemed by love di - vine,
been re-deemed! I'm redeemed by love divine,

Glo-ry, glo-ry,Christ is mine,Christ is mine, All to him I
Christ is mine, All to him

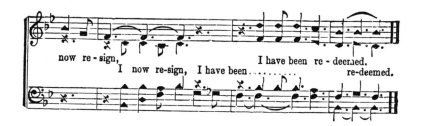

now re-sign, I have been re-deemed.
I now re-sign, I have been.......... re-deemed.

Why Not Now? 124

Daniel W. Whittle

Charles C. Case

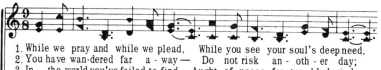

1. While we pray and while we plead, While you see your soul's deep need,
2. You have wan-dered far a - way— Do not risk an - oth - er day;
3. In the world you've failed to find Aught of peace for trou-bled mind;
4. Come to Christ, con-fes - sion make—Come to Christ and par - don take;

While your Fa - ther calls you home, Will you not, my broth - er, come?
Do not turn from God your face, But to - day ac-cept His grace.
Come to Christ, on Him be-lieve— Peace and joy you shall re - ceive.
Trust in Him from day to day— He will keep you all the way.

CHORUS

Why not now? why not now? Why not come to Je-sus now? Je-sus now?
Why not now? why not now?

125   Some Glad Day

W. M. R.

Will M. Ramsey
Arranged John T. Benson, Jr.

1. O bless-ed tho't...... sweet rest will come,.... Some glad day
2. These heav-y loads....... we shall lay down,.....
3. Our suff'ring too....... will soon be past,.....
4. All war and strife...... will soon be o'er. .....

Some glad day

aft-er while;   When all our toil....... on earth is done,......
When we re-ceive...... our heav'nly crown,.....
When we shall find...... sweet rest at last,.......
aft-er while; We'll find sweet peace...... on heaven's shore,......

CHORUS

There'll come a glad day   aft-er while.   O aft-er
aft-er while.

while,   aft-er while,   There'll come a glad day
Aft-er while,   aft-er while,

aft-er while;   O aft-er while,   aft-er while,
aft-er while;   Aft-er while,   aft-er while.

There'll come a glad day aft - er while.

aft - er while.

Old Time Power 126

C. D. T.

Charlie D. Tillman

1. They were in an up - per chamber, They were all with one ac-cord,
2. Yes, this pow'r from Heav'n descended, With the sound of rush - ing wind;
3. Yes, this "old-time" pow'r was given, To our fa - thers who were true;

When the Ho - ly Ghost de - scend - ed, As was prom-ised by our Lord.
Tongues of fire came down up - on them, As the Lord said He would send.
This is promised to be - liev-ers, And we all may have it, too.

CHORUS

O Lord, send the pow'r just now! O Lord, send the pow'r just now!

O Lord, send the pow'r just now, And bap-tize ev - 'ry one!

127   I Can Tell You the Time

A. M. P.

Adger M. Pace

Very slow.

1. I remember the time.......... when in darkness I wan-dered, far-ther from home,
2. Just a sin-ner was I.............. far a-way from my Saviour, go-ing a - lone,
3. I can nev-er for-get.......... when He spoke to me gently "follow thou me"

On the mountain of sin,.............. I had traveled so long, I had traveled so long;
With no hope of reward............ at the end of the way, at the end of the way;
In the fountain of life,.......... there's a balm for your soul, there's a balm for your soul;

Like the prod-i - gal son,.......... all my goods I had squandered, sad-ly I'd roam,
But the Saviour came down,.......... and He gave me His fa-vor, all for my own,
So I heed-ed His voice,.......... He was speaking in-tent-ly, glad-ly I see,

But the Saviour came in.............. and He gave me a song 'twas a beau-ti-ful song.
Now I'm singing His praise,.......... for He saved me that day, tru-ly saved me that day.
Thru His marvelous grace,.......... I am happy and whole, I am hap-py and whole.

CHORUS.

I can tell you now, the time,   I can tell you the time,   I can

128 I've Never Been This Homesick Before

D. R.

Dottie Rambo

1. There's a light in the win - dow, the ta - ble's
2. I can see the fam - 'ly gath - er, sweet fa - ces

spread in splen - dor; Some - one's stand - ing by the o - pen
all fa - mil - iar; No one's old or fee - ble an - y -

door. I can see a crys - tal riv - er
more. This lone - some heart is cry - ing;

So I must be near for - ev - er. Lord, I've
Think I'll spread my wings for fly - ing. Lord, I've

nev - er been this home - sick be - fore.

CHORUS

See the bright Light shine,_____ It's just a - bout home time,_____ I can see my Fa - ther stand - ing at the door._____ This world's_ been a wil - der - ness,_____ I'm read - y for de - liv - er - ance._____ Lord, I've nev - er been this home - sick be - fore._____

129 Open My Eyes

C. H.

Candy Hemphill

1. ___ Lord, I saw ___ how You used ole Mo-
2. Lord, have Your way; ___ ___ I'm just a ves-sel

ses, How he led Your ___ chil-dren
that You made, ___ I don't have a lot to

out ___ of mis - er - y; ___ But I'm un-
of - fer, I'm just clay; ___ But let me

worth - y ___ to do ___ such a deed, But
see ___ just what You would have me be,

while I'm here, ___ I'm sure there's a
Give me the word, and I'll say what You'd

CHORUS

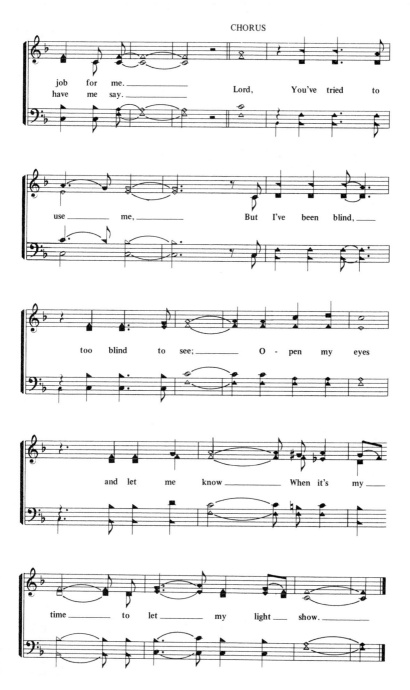

job for me. _____
have me say. _____ Lord, You've tried to

use _____ me, _____ But I've been blind, _____

too blind to see; _____ O- pen my eyes

and let me know _____ When it's my _____

time _____ to let _____ my light _____ show. _____

130 When God Dips His Love in My Heart

C. D.

Cleavant Derricks

1. When God dips His pen of love in my heart And
2. Some-times tho' the way is drear-y, dark and cold, And
3. He walked ev-'ry step up Cal-v'ry's rug-ged way To

writes my soul a mes-sage He wants me to know, His Spir-it
some un-bur-dened sor-row keeps me from the goal, I go to
give His life com-plete-ly, and bring a bet-ter day; My life was

all di-vine fills this sin-ful soul of mine, *D.S.*—hal-le-lu-jah! When
God in prayer, I can al-ways find Him there, To
steeped in sin, but in love He took me in, His

Fine CHORUS

God dips His love in my heart.
whis-per sweet peace to my soul. Well, I said I wouldn't
blood washed a-way ev-'ry stain.

tell it to a liv-ing soul How He bro't sal-va-tion when He made me

whole, But I found I couldn't hide such love as Je - sus did im-part;

D.S.

Laugh and it makes me cry,   sets my sin-ful soul on fire,
'Cause it makes me   then it

Revive Us Again   131

Wm. P. Mackay   John J. Husband

1. We praise Thee, O God, for the Son of Thy love, For   Je-sus who
2. We praise Thee, O God, for Thy Spir - it of light, Who has shown us the
3. All glo - ry and praise to the Lamb that was slain, Who has borne all our
4. Re - vive us a - gain, Fill each heart with Thy love, May each soul be re-

CHORUS

died and is now gone a-bove.
Sav - ior and scat-tered our night.
sins, and has cleansed ev'-ry stain. Hal-le - lu - jah! Thine the glo - ry, Hal - le-
kin-dled with fire from a - bove.

lu - jah! A-men! Hal - le - lu-jah! Thine the glo - ry, Re-vive us a-gain.

132 Standing by the River

Albert E. Brumley
Cho. M. W. E.

Marion W. Easterling

1. Here I stand be-side death's chill-y wa-ters wait-ing for my fi-nal call,
2. Mu-sic from the land of end-less glo-ry fall up-on my list'ning ear,
3. Shad-ows of the night are swift-ly fall-ing, lo I hear the boatman's oar,

Standing by the riv-er look-ing be-yond;

Stand-ing by the riv-er   look-ing be-yond;

Gaz-ing t'ward the land of fade-less beau-ty where no surg-es rise and fall,
Fac-es of my friends I oft-en vi-sion, forms of loved ones oft ap-pear,
Man-y are the voic-es sweet-ly call-ing, I must tar-ry here no more,

Stand-ing by the riv-er   look-ing be-yond.

Stand-ing by the riv-er   look-ing be-yond.

Chorus

Stand-ing by the riv-er   waiting for the boatman,

Standing by the riv-er   waiting for the boatman,

List'ning to the mu-sic on the oth-er shore;

List'ning to the mu-sic   the oth-er shore;

I can hear the an-gels   singing out a welcome,

I can hear the an-gels   sing-ing out a welcome,

With my friends and loved ones   who have gone be-fore.

With my friends and loved ones   gone on be-fore.

We Thank Thee, Lord   133

Albert H. Hutchinson   Robert N. Quails

1. For all the bless-ings of the year, For all the friends we hold so
2. For life and health, those com-mon things, Which ev-ery day and hour
3. For love of Thine, which nev - er tires, Which all our bet - ter thought in-

dear, For peace on earth, both far and near, We thank Thee, Lord.
brings, For home, where our af - fec - tion clings, We thank Thee, Lord.
spires And warms our lives with Heav'n-ly fires, We thank Thee, Lord.

134   I'm Free Again

V. B. E.

V. B. (Vep) Ellis

1. Sa-tan led my soul a-stray (Satan led my soul a-stray I drift-ed),
2. On the sin-ful path be-low (on the sin-ful path be-low is trou-ble),
3. Soon the pearl-y gates I'll see (soon the pearl-y gates I'll see in heav-en),

From the straight and nar - row way (that leads to hap-pi-ness and life e-
All in sor-row, grief and woe, (the sin-ner's load is might-y hard to
Soon I'll live e-ter-nal-ly (And then I'll nev-er die but live for-

ter - nal); But to Je-sus I did pray,(to the Lord I hum-bly pray'd),
car,- ry); But I've left the shift-ing sand, (I have left the shift-ing sand),
ev - er); Friends and loved ones wait for me,(friends and loved ones wait for me),

He heard my prayer, res-cued me that ver - y day, (that ver - y day).
Up - on the Rock, sol - id Rock, I'll take my stand, (I'll take my stand).
I'll sail up high, thru the sky, be-cause I'm free, (be-cause I'm free).

CHORUS

Praise God I'm free, I've been set free by the grace of God; I'm free,

Free from ev - 'ry chain of sin, with a set - tled peace with - in,

No more the paths of sin I trod; I'm free,

The blood has cleansed ev - 'ry sin - ful stain; I'm free,

Heav-en's gates I'll en - ter in,

I'm free a - gain.

Praise the liv - ing God, I'm free a - gain.

135
Light the Light

J. S.

John Stallings
Arr. by W. Elmo Mercer

where; _____ They say that things are hope-less and they just breathe a lit-tle
meet; _____ _____ There are peo-ple wait-ing _____ now for you and me to

pray'r. But there is some-thing that we all can do a-bout the
greet. _____ Let a lit-tle hap-pi-ness just shine a-cross your

scene; _____ Lis-ten now and I'll tell you what I
face; _____ We can make _____ this world a bet-ter

⊕ CODA

mean. _____ Light the light. _____ Ev-'ry-
place. _____

bod-y do your part and light _____ the light! _____

136 Thank God I Am Free

J. McF

James McFall

1. For a long time I trav - eled _____ down a long, lone - ly road, _____ my _ heart was so heav - y _____ in sin I sank low; _____ Then I heard a - bout Je - sus, _____ What a won - der - ful hour, _____ I'm so glad that I found out He would bring me out through His sav - ing pow'r. _____

2. Like a bird out of pri - son _____ that's _ tak - en His flight, _____ lone - ly road like the blind man that God _____ gave back His sight; _____ Like the poor wretch-ed beg - gar _____ That's found for - tune and fame, _____ I'm so glad that I found out He would bring me out through His Ho - ly name. _____

won - drous hour
for - tune, fame

CHORUS

Thank God I am free, free, free from this world of sin, _____ Wash'd in the blood of Je - sus been born a - gain; _____ Hal - le - lu - jah, I'm saved, saved, saved By His won - der - ful grace, _____ I'm so glad that I found out He would bring me out and show me the way. _____

137 There's a Whole Lot of People Going Home

D. I.

David Ingles

1. There will be those ___ who are miss - ing, You'd ___
2. Some will go in - to a pan - ic, Cry - ing,
3. I ___ can see Him at the ta - ble, ___

think ___ ev - 'ry - bod - y would know; ___
"Sing an - oth - er verse of that song"; ___
Al - most ___ read - y to say, "Come!" ___

But they'll still be too bus - y go - ing no - where, ___
Say - ing, "Lord, here am I, ___ now I'm read - y!" ___
Know - ing well there will be no va - cant set - tings, ___

They won't e - ven no - tice that we're gone. ___
But their last op - por - tu - ni - ty is gone. ___
'Cause the rest of the fam - 'ly's com - ing home. ___

There's a whole lot of peo - ple go - ing home!

By the signs of time it won't be long; _____

In the twin - kling of an eye we'll all __ be __ gone, _____

There's a whole lot of peo - ple go - ing home!

138 I Want to Be Ready to Meet Him

Adger M. Pace

G. T. Speer

1. You may have your worldly pleas-ures, your sil - ver and your gold, You may
2. You may talk a - bout your rich - es, your diamonds and your pearls, You may
3. There is one thing I can boast of, sal - va - tion from the fall, I'm an

pile up all the rich - es that this old world can hold; But I'd rath - er
gain the wealth for a - ges of this and all the worlds, But the Sav-iour
heir to wealth in glo - ry, my Fa - ther owns it all; That is why I'm

D. S.—to meet Him in the sky; Oh, I want to

have my Sav - iour, and with Him firm - ly stand, For I want to be
is more pre-cious, with Him I'll take my stand, For I want to be
shout-ing hap - py and go at His com-mand, For I want to be

be more like Him, and do His blest com-mand, For I want to be

FINE. CHORUS.

read - y to meet Him in the glo - ry land. I want to be
I want to be

D. S.

read - y to meet Him by and by, I want to be read - y
read - y I want to be read - y

That Glad Reunion Day

139

A. M. P.

Adger M. Pace

1. There will be a hap-py meet-ing in heav-en I know,
2. There with-in the ho-ly cit-y we'll sing and re-joice,
3. When we live a mil-lion years in that won-der-ful place,

When we see the ma-ny loved ones we've known here be-low,
Prais-ing Christ the bless-ed Sav-iour with heart and with voice,
Bask-ing in the love of Je-sus, be-hold-ing His face,

Gath-er on the bless-ed hill-tops with hearts all a-glow,
Tell Him how we came to love Him and make Him our choice,
It will seem but just a mo-ment of prais-ing His grace,

D.S.-There with all the ho-ly an-gels and loved ones to stay,

FINE   CHORUS

That will be a glad re-un-ion day.   Glad   day,   a
                          That will be a hap-py day, yes, a

That will be a glad re-un-ion day.

D.S.

won-der-ful day, Glad   day,   a   glo-ri-ous day;
won-der-ful day, That will be a hap-py day, yes, a   glo-ri-ous day;

140 The Blood that Stained the Old Rugged Cross

A. E. B.

Albert E. Brumley

1. On the cross of Cal - va - ry our bless-ed Sav - ior died, Gave His
2. To the cross, the rug - ged cross they nailed His pre-cious hands, And in
3. What an aw - ful death He died to par - don you and me, All a -

life to save the world from loss; In His pain and ag - o - ny, for ev-'ry
death He ful - ly paid the cost, There is par - don in His love for ev-'ry
lone in ag - o - ny He tossed, And a world once lost in sin can now be

Fine CHORUS

sin to hide, Shed the
one that stands For the blood that stained the old rug-ged cross. 'Twas His
whol - ly free By the

blood, His precious blood that stained the old rug-ged cross, 'Twas His love that paid the

D.S.

aw - ful cost; O soul so far a - stray come and plunge to-day In the

Hide Me, Rock of Ages

B.C.G.

Brantley C. George

1. O thou blessed Rock of A-ges, (Rock of A-ges, I am) Trust-ing
2. Keep me when the storm-clouds gather, (storm-clouds gath-er, keep me) Till the
3. When my journey is com-plet-ed, (is com-plet-ed, Sav-ior) And there's

now dear Lord in Thee; (dear Lord in Thee I'm trusting) Keep me till my
sun comes shin-ing thru; (comes shining thru the shadows) Keep me till my
no more work to do; (no work to do, O bless-ed) Sav-ior guide my

D. S.-When the storm a-
FINE

jour-ney's end-ed, (journey's ended, Keep me) Till Thy blessed face I see.
work is o-ver, (work is o-ver, Keep me) Till I bid this world a-dieu.
wea-ry spir-it, (wea-ry spir-it, To that) Hap-py land be-yond the blue.

round me rag-es, (round me rag-es, Bless-ed) Rock of A-ges hide Thou me.

REFRAIN

Hide me, O blest Rock of A - - - ges,
A - ges, Rock of A - ges, hide me,

D. S.

Till Thy bless-ed face I see; (Thy face I see, in glo-ry)

142   Closer to You

D. C.

Dave Clark

1. I know that I've failed you, Lord, time and a - gain.
2. ___ Lord, I sur - ren - der all that I am,

But each time You al - ways stayed true; ___
For what - ev - er You'd have me do; ___

And that's why I kneel at the cross once a - gain,
I've faith in Your prom - ise, I know that You'll show

And ask to draw clos - er to You. ___
A way to draw clos - er to You. ___

CHORUS

Clos - er to You, Lord, ___ Clos - er I pray,

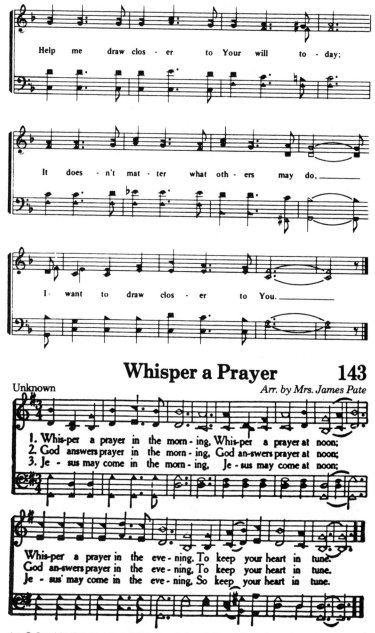

Help me draw clos-er to Your will to-day;

It does-n't mat-ter what oth-ers may do, _____

I want to draw clos-er to You. _____

Whisper a Prayer 143

Unknown

Arr. by Mrs. James Pate

1. Whis-per a prayer in the morn-ing, Whis-per a prayer at noon;
2. God answers prayer in the morn-ing, God an-swers prayer at noon;
3. Je-sus may come in the morn-ing, Je-sus may come at noon;

Whis-per a prayer in the eve-ning, To keep your heart in tune.
God an-swers prayer in the eve-ning, To keep your heart in tune.
Je-sus' may come in the eve-ning, So keep your heart in tune.

144   I'll Meet You by the River

A. E. B.

Albert E. Brumley

1. O - ver on the bright E - ly - sian shore, Where the howling tempest comes no more,
2. Aft - er all the sor - row and the strife, Aft - er all the trou - ble of this life,
3. Aft - er all the dis - ap - point - ments here, Aft - er all the shadows dis - ap - pear,

I'll meet you by the riv - er
Meet you by the riv - er   some hap - py day;
some sweet day;

Far be - yond the partings and the tomb, Where the charming ros - es ev - er bloom,
When we gath - er far be - yond the sea, What a hap - py meet - ing that will be,
When the eve - ning sun at last goes down, When we go to wear a robe and crown,

I'll meet you by the riv - er
Meet you by the riv - er some sweet day.
some hap - py day.

CHORUS

I'll meet you by the riv - er
Meet you by the riv - er   some hap - py day,
some sweet day,

Bright and shining riv-er so far a-way;
By the bright and shining riv-er far a-way;

Aft-er we have flown these prison bars to a cit-y far be-yond the stars,

Meet you by the riv-er some sweet day.
I'll meet you by the riv-er some hap-py day.

Blest Be the Tie

145

John Fawcett

Hans G. Nageli

1. Blest be the tie that binds Our hearts in Chris-tian love;
2. Be-fore our Fa-ther's throne, We pour our ar-dent pray'rs;
3. We share our mu-tual woes, Our mu-tual bur-dens bear;
4. When we a-sun-der part, It gives us in-ward pain;

The fel-low-ship of kin-dred minds Is like to that a-bove.
Our fears, our hopes, our aims are one, Our com-forts and our cares.
And oft-en for each oth-er flows The sym-pa-thiz-ing tear.
But we shall still be joined in heart, And hope to meet a-gain.

146 When it's Time

R. L. H.

Roger L. Horne

1. We have heard a-bout His com-ing for so long, ___
2. Through the years we've seen the Scrip-tures all ful-filled, ___

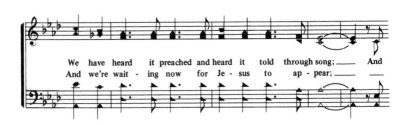

We have heard it preached and heard it told through song; ___ And
And we're wait-ing now for Je-sus to ap-pear; ___ ___

though I do not know the time, ___ ___ still I know ___
Soon the saints of all the a-ges will join the song of

this, for sure, He'll re-turn a-gain for me some glo-rious
vic-to-ry, Prais-ing Je - sus will be our end-less

CHORUS

day! _____ When it's time _____ He will
theme! _____ When it's time

come, _____ Then we'll know _____ the
He will come, Then we'll know

bat - tle's been won; _____ We will lay our ar - mor

down, _____ and pick up our robe and crown, Then we'll go

home to be with Je - sus, when it's time! _____

147   **Heavenly Love**

Title suggested by Bill Baker, Louisville, Ky.

V. B. E.   V. B. (Vep) Ellis

1. Heav - en - ly love.............. was all that could help me,.................. I was a - stray............. so sad and a - lone;.................. I looked a - bove.............. my bur - dens all left me,.................. Now I can say,.............. "Heav-en's my home"..............

2. Trou - bles of earth (repeat words of soprano) so of - ten o'er - take me,..............Bur - dens of life............. with heart - ache and care;..............Heav - en - ly love............. will nev - er for - sake me,.............. Fill - ing my need,.............. Je - sus is there..............

3. When I shall stand.................. at Jor - dan's dark riv - er,..............Shad - ows of night.............. are gath - 'ring a - bove;..............There is a pow'r.............. I know will de - liv - er,.............. Heav - en - ly love,.............. heav - en - ly love..............

CHORUS

Heav - en - ly love, the love of my
Heav - en - ly love the

Lord, Lift - ing a - bove for
love of my Sav - ior, Lift - ing a - bove

He is my sword and shield; Giv - ing me light in
my sword and shield; Giv - ing me light

dark - ness of night, Heav - en - ly
in dark - ness of night,

love, heav - en - ly love.
Heav - en - ly love, heav - en - ly love.

148 These Are They

S. P., Jr.

Squire Parsons, Jr.

1. While up-on ____ the isle ____ of Pat-mos, ____ John be-held ____ a glo-rious sight; ____ A num-ber which ____ no man ____ could num-ber, ____ Prais-ing God ____ both day ____ and night. ____

2. Nev-er-more ____ will they ____ know hun-ger, ____ Nev-er-more ____ will they ____ know pain; ____ No tears will ev-er dim ____ their vis-ion, ____ No sad good-byes ____ be said ____ a-gain. ____

These are they _____ who've won ___ the bat - tle, _____ These are they _____ who've stood ___ the test; _____ Robed in gar - ments pure ___ and spot - less, The re - deemed, _____ the pure ___ and blest. _____

149   I'll Live In Glory

J. M. H.

J. M. Henson

1. I'd like to stay here long-er than man's al-lot-ted days, And watch the fleeting
2. I want to be of serv-ice a-long this pilgrim way, And lead the lost to
3. The end I know is near-ing, by faith I look a-way, To yon-der home su-

chang-es of life's un-e-ven ways; But if my Sav-ior calls me to
Je - sus as fer-vent-ly I pray; As day by day I trav-el I'll
per - nal, the land of end-less day; I'll cling to Him for-ev - er and

that sweet home on high, I'll live with Him for-ev - er in glo-ry by and by.
keep Him ev - er nigh, And live with Him for-ev - er in glo-ry by and by.
look be-yond the sky, And live with Him for-ev - er in glo-ry by and by.

CHORUS

O yes, I'll live in glo-ry   by   and   by, I'll tell and sing love's
live in glo-ry by and by,

sto - ry   there   on   high; There with my dear Redeem-er   no
tell love's sto-ry there on high;   there no

more to die, O yes, I'll live in glo-ry by and by.
no more to die, glo-ry by and by.

Precious Memories

150

Words and Melody J. B. F. Wright

Arr for John T. Benson, Jr.

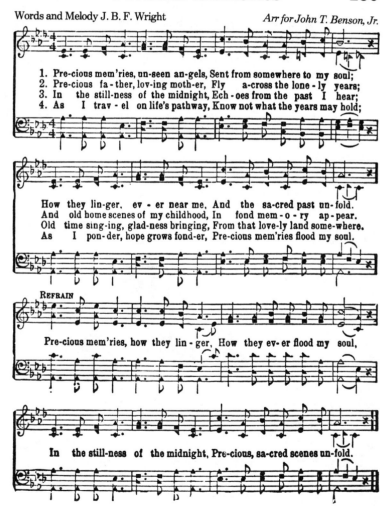

1. Pre-cious mem'ries, un-seen an-gels, Sent from somewhere to my soul;
2. Pre-cious fa-ther, lov-ing moth-er, Fly a-cross the lone-ly years;
3. In the still-ness of the midnight, Ech-oes from the past I hear;
4. As I trav-el on life's pathway, Know not what the years may hold;

How they lin-ger, ev-er near me, And the sa-cred past un-fold.
And old home scenes of my childhood, In fond mem-o-ry ap-pear.
Old time sing-ing, glad-ness bringing, From that love-ly land some-where.
As I pon-der, hope grows fond-er, Pre-cious mem'ries flood my soul.

REFRAIN

Pre-cious mem'ries, how they lin-ger, How they ev-er flood my soul,

In the still-ness of the midnight, Pre-cious, sa-cred scenes un-fold.

151 Living by Faith

James Wells, 4th vs. R. E. W.

J. L. Heath

1. I care not to-day what the morrow may bring, If shadow or sunshine or rain,
2. Tho' tempests may blow and the storm-clouds arise, Obscuring the brightness of life,
3. I know that He safely will carry me thro', No matter what e-vils be-tide,
4. Our Lord will return to this earth some sweet day, Our troubles will then all be o'er,

The Lord I know rul-eth o'er ev-er-y-thing, And all of my wor-ry is vain.
I'm nev-er a-larmed at the overcast skies, The Master looks on at the strife.
Why should I then care, tho' the tempest may blow, If Je-sus walks close to my side.
The Mas-ter so gent-ly will lead us a-way, Beyond that blest heav'nly shore.

REFRAIN.

Liv-ing by faith,............ in Je-sus a-bove,............
Yes, liv-ing by faith,

in Je-sus a-bove,

Trusting, con-fid - - ing in His great love;............
Trusting, con-fid-ing

yes, in His great love;

From all harm safe.............. in His shel-ter-ing arm,..............
Safe from all harm, safe

His shel-ter-ing arm.

I Feel Like Traveling On 152

Wm. Hunter, D. D.

Arr. by James D. Vaughan

With feeling.

1. My heav-'nly home is bright and fair, I feel like trav-el-ing on,
2. Its glit-t'ring-tow'rs the sun out-shine, I feel like trav-el-ing on,
3. Let oth-ers seek a home be-low, I feel like trav-el-ing on,
4. The Lord has been so good to me, I feel like trav-el-ing on,

Nor pain, nor death can en-ter there, I feel like travel-ing on.
That heav'nly mansion shall be mine, I feel like travel-ing on.
Which flames devour, or waves o'erflow, I feel like travel-ing on.
Un-til that bless-ed home I see, I feel like travel-ing on.

REFRAIN.

Yes, I feel like trav-el-ing on, I feel like trav-el-ing
trav-el-ing on,

on; My heav'nly home is bright and fair, I feel like traveling on.
travel-ing on;

153   I'll Be a Friend to Jesus

Rev. Johnson Oatman   J. W. Dennis

1. They tried my Lord.......... and Mas-ter, With no one to .... de-
2. The world may turn.......... a-gainst Him, I'll love Him to.......... the
3. I'll do what He.......... may bid me; I'll go where He..........may
4. To all who need.......... a Sav-ior, My Friend I rec - - - om-

fend; With-in the halls...... of Pi - late He stood without......
end, And while on earth......I'm liv - ing, My Lord shall have......
send; I'll try each fly - - ing mo-ment To prove that I'm...... His
mend, Be-cause He bro't...... sal - va - tion, Is why I am...... His

Chorus

friend. I'll be a friend.............. to Je - sus,
I'll be a friend to Je - sus,

My life for Him.............. I'll spend; I'll be a friend..........
My life for Him I'll spend; I'll be a friend

to Je - sus, Un-til my years.............. shall end.
to Je - sus, Un - til my years shall end.

If I Could Hear My Mother Pray Again 154

James Rowe

J. W. Vaughan

1. How sweet and hap-py seem those days of which I dream, When mem-o-ry re-calls them now and then! And with what rap-ture sweet my wea-ry heart would beat, If I could hear my moth-er pray a-gain.

2. She used to pray that I on Je-sus would re-ly, And al-ways walk the shin-ing gos-pel way; So trust-ing still His love I seek that home a-bove, Where I shall meet my moth-er some glad day.

3. With-in the old home-place, her pa-tient, smil-ing face Was al-ways spread-ing com-fort, hope and cheer; And when she used to sing to her e-ter-nal King, It was the songs the an-gels loved to hear.

4. Her work on earth is done, the life-crown has been won, And she will be at rest with Him a-bove; And some glad morn-ing, she I know will wel-come me To that e-ter-nal home of peace and love.

D. S.-so much to me, If I could hear my mother pray a-gain.

CHORUS

If I could hear my moth-er pray a-gain, If I could
If I could on-ly If I could on-ly
If I could on-ly hear

hear her ten-der voice as then! So glad I'd be, 'twould mean
hap-py I should
So hap-py I should be

155 Won't it be Wonderful There?

James Rowe   Homer F. Morris

1. When with the Sav - ior we en - ter the glo - ry-land, Won't it be
2. Walk - ing and talk - ing with Christ, the su - per - nal One, Won't it be
3. There where the tem-pest will nev - er be sweep-ing us, Won't it be

won- der - ful there? End - ed the trou - bles and cares of the sto - ry-land,
won- der - ful there? Prais- ing, a - dor-ing the matchless e - ter-nal One,
won- der - ful there? Sure that for - ev - er the Lord will be keep-ing us,

Refrain

Won't it be won-der-ful there? Won't it be won-der-ful there,
                                                wonderful there,

Hav-ing no bur-dens to bear?...... Joy - ous - ly sing-ing with
                   o - ver there?

heart-bells all ring-ing, O won't it be won-der - ful there?
                                                won-der-ful there?

I'll Fly Away

156

A. E. B.

Albert E. Brumley

1. Some glad morn-ing when this life is o'er, I'll fly a-
2. When the shad-ows of this life have grown,
3. Just a few more wea - ry days and then, fly a-way

way;
fly a - way;

To a home on God's ce - les - tial shore,
Like a bird from pris - on bars has flown,
To a land where joys shall nev - er end,

CHORUS

I'll fly a - way.
fly a - way, fly a - way.
I'll fly a-way,
fly a - way,
fly a -

way, O glo - ry, I'll fly a - way;
fly a - way, in the morn-ing,
When I die,

Hal - le-lu - jah, by and by, I'll fly a-way.
fly a - way, fly a - way.

157 I Should Have Been Crucified

G. J.

Gordon Jensen

1. I was guilty with noth-ing to say, And they were
2. Crown of thorns, the spear deep in His side, And the

com-ing to take me a-way, But then a
pain should have been mine, The rust-y

voice from heaven was heard that said, "Let him go!
nails were meant for me, (O,) yet Christ took them and

CHORUS

Take me in-stead!" And I should have been cru-ci-fied!
let me go free!

I should have suf-fered and died! I should have hung on the
Oo

cross in dis-grace, But Je-sus, God's Son, took my place!—

Savior, More Than Life 158

Fanny J. Crosby

W. H. Doane

1. Sav - ior, more than life to me, I am cling-ing, cling-ing close to Thee;
2. Thro' this changing world below, Lead me gent-ly, gent-ly as I go;
3. Let me love Thee more and more, Till this fleeting, fleeting life is o'er;

Let Thy pre-cious blood ap-plied, Keep me ev - er, ev - er near Thy side.
Trust-ing Thee, I can-not stray, I can nev - er, nev - er lose my way.
Till my soul is lost in love, In a bright-er, bright-er world a-bove.

D.S. - May Thy ten-der love to me, Bind me clos - er, clos - er, Lord to Thee.

CHORUS

D.S.

Ev-'ry day, ev - 'ry hour, Let me feel Thy cleansing power;
Ev-'ry day and hour, ev - 'ry day and hour,

159 Victory in Jesus

E. M. B.

E. M. Bartlett

1. I heard an old, old sto - ry How a Sav - ior came from glo - ry,
2. I heard a - bout His heal - ing, Of His cleansing pow'r re-veal-ing,
3. I heard a - bout a man-sion He has built for me in glo - ry,

How He gave His life on Cal - va - ry To save a wretch like me;
How He made the lame to walk a - gain And caused the blind to see;
And I heard a - bout the streets of gold Be - yond the crys - tal sea;

I heard a - bout His groan-ing, Of His pre - cious blood's a-ton - ing,
And then I cried, "dear Je - sus, Come and heal my bro - ken spir - it,"
A - bout the an - gels sing-ing And the old re - demp-tion sto - ry,

Then I re - pent - ed of my sins And won the vic - to - ry.
And some - how Je - sus came and bro't To me the vic - to - ry.
And some sweet day I'll sing up there The song of vic - to - ry.

CHORUS

O vic-to - ry in Je - sus, My Sav - ior, for - ev - er, He sought me and

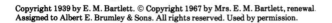

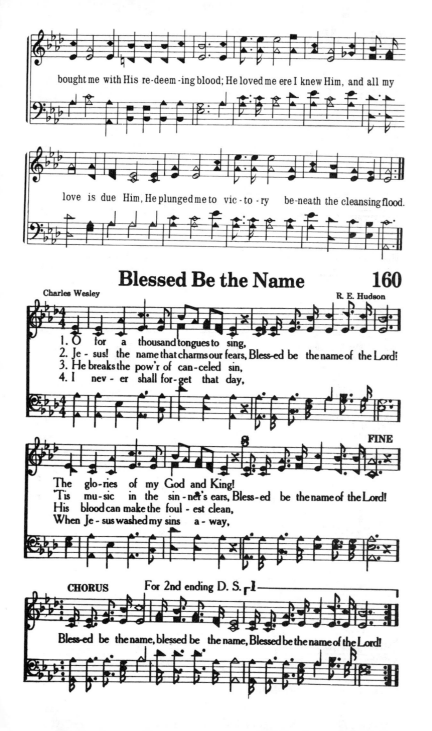

bought me with His re-deem-ing blood; He loved me ere I knew Him, and all my

love is due Him, He plunged me to vic-to-ry be-neath the cleansing flood.

Blessed Be the Name 160

Charles Wesley

R. E. Hudson

1. O for a thousand tongues to sing,
2. Je - sus! the name that charms our fears, Bless-ed be the name of the Lord!
3. He breaks the pow'r of can-celed sin,
4. I nev - er shall for-get that day,

FINE

The glo-ries of my God and King!
'Tis mu-sic in the sin-ner's ears, Bless-ed be the name of the Lord!
His blood can make the foul - est clean,
When Je - sus washed my sins a - way,

CHORUS For 2nd ending D. S.

Bless-ed be the name, blessed be the name, Blessed be the name of the Lord!

161 Way Down Deep in My Soul

F. E. H.

Floyd E. Hunter

1. I have a feel-ing in my soul, Since the Sav-ior made me whole,
2. A bright and hap-py glad new song, I'll be sing-ing all a-long,
3. A light of heav'n I now can see, For He came and set me free,

Way down, way down, A-way down deep in my soul;
Way down, way down, my soul;

I'm trust-ing Je-sus ev-'ry day, For I know I'm on my way,
For Je-sus saved my soul at last, And I know He'll hold me fast,
I know there's glo-ry to be-hold, For I feel it in my soul,

D.S.—Then I'll be go-ing to that home, Nev-er more from Him to roam,

FINE

Way down, way down, Yes, a-way down in my soul.
Way down, way down, my soul.

CHORUS

Down in my soul, I'll sing and pray,
Down in my soul, I'll sing and pray,

'Til Christ shall come, To take me with Him to stay;
'Til Christ shall come, to stay;

Hold to God's Unchanging Hand 162

Jennie Wilson

F. L. Eiland
Arranged by John T. Benson, Jr.

1. Time is filled with swift transi-tion, Naught of earth unmoved can stand, Build your
2. Trust in Him who will not leave you, What-so-ev-er years may bring, If by
3. Cov-et not this world's vain rich-es, That so rap-id-ly de-cay, Seek to
4. When your journey is com-plet-ed, If to God you have been true, Fair and

CHORUS

hopes on things e-ter-nal, Hold to God's unchanging hand! Hold
earth-ly friends for-sak-en, Still more close-ly to Him cling!
gain the heav'n-ly treas-ures, They will nev-er pass a-way!
bright the home in glo-ry, Your en-rap-tured soul will view! Hold to His hand,

to God's un-chang-ing hand! Hold
Hold to His hand!
to God's un-chang-

Rit.

ing hand! Build your hopes on things e-ter-nal, Hold to God's unchanging hand!

163 I'll Meet You in the Morning

A. E. B.

Albert E. Brumley

1. I will meet you in the morn-ing, by the bright riv - er side, When all
2. I will meet you in the morn-ing, in the sweet by and by, And ex -
3. I will meet you in the morn-ing, at the end of the way, On the

sor - row has drift - ed a - way; I'll be stand-ing at the por-tals,
change the old cross for a crown; There will be no dis-ap - point-ments
streets of that cit - y of gold; Where we all can be to - geth - er

when the gates o - pen wide, At the close of life's long, dreary day.
and no - bod - y shall die, In that land where the sun go - eth down.
and be hap - py for aye, While the years and the a - ges shall roll.

CHORUS

Meet you in the morn - ing, meet you in the morn - ing,
I'll meet you in the morn - ing,

"How do you do," "How do you do,"
with a "How do you do," and we'll

164 Jesus, Have Mercy on Me

J. H.

Joel Hemphill

1. I'm not e-ven worth-y of all of the bless-ings _____ I've had while
2. _ Lord, I'm down here _ where You used to be _____ But I've failed all the

liv-ing be-low_____ So when I think of heav-en and all of its
tests that You passed, _ _____ And so I won't _ be first in the

splen-dor, I know I'm not worth-y to go;_____ Though _ fee-bly I've
race,_____ but "run it" was all that You asked;_____ And when I stand be-

tried _____ to do what You've want-ed and be what You'd have me to be, When You
fore You on that fi-nal day, _ then I'm sure _ You'll plain-ly see, _ It's not

make up Your jew-els and call in Your own, Je-sus, have mer-cy on me!
jus-tice I'm need-ing,but mer-cy, O Lord, Je-sus, have mer-cy on me!

CHORUS

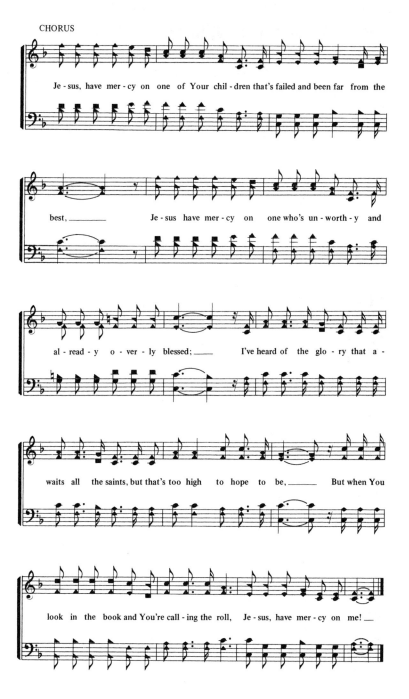

Je-sus, have mer-cy on one of Your chil-dren that's failed and been far from the best, _____ Je-sus have mer-cy on one who's un-worth-y and al-read-y o-ver-ly blessed; _____ I've heard of the glo-ry that a-waits all the saints, but that's too high to hope to be, _____ But when You look in the book and You're call-ing the roll, Je-sus, have mer-cy on me! __

165 Love Grew Where the Blood Fell

J. S.

John Stallings

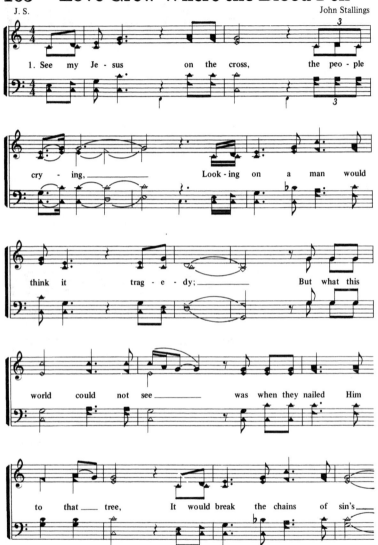

1. See my Je - sus on the cross, the peo - ple cry - ing, _____ Look - ing on a man would think it trag - e - dy; _____ But what this world could not see _____ was when they nailed Him to that ___ tree, It would break the chains of sin's

Thorns of violence and hate were growing wildly,
And the sorrow they had caused was plain to see;
But when that blood came streaming down that cross
where my Jesus bled and died,
It started blossoms of forgiveness growing free!

CHORUS

cap - tiv - i - ty. Love grew where the blood fell; Flow'rs of hope sprang up for men in mis - er - y; Sin died where the blood fell; I'm so glad this pre - cious blood has cov - ered me!

166

Jesus Hold My Hand

A. E. B.

Albert E. Brumley

1. As I trav-el thru this pil-grim land There is a Friend who
2. Let me trav-el in the light di-vine That I may see the
3. When I wan-der thru the val-ley dim To-ward the set-ting

walks with me, Leads me safe-ly thro' the sink-ing sand, It is the
bless-ed way; Keep me that I may be whol-ly Thine And sing re-
of the sun, Lead me safe-ly to a land of rest If I a

Christ of Cal-va-ry; This would be my pray'r, dear Lord, each
demption's song some day; I will be a sol-dier brave and
crown of life have won; I have put my faith in Thee, dear

day To help me do the best I can, For I need Thy light to
true And ev-er firm-ly take a stand, As I on-ward go and
Lord, That I may reach the gold-en strand, There's no oth-er friend on

guide me day and night Bless-ed Je-sus, hold my hand.
dai-ly meet the foe, Bless-ed Je-sus, hold my hand.
whom I can de-pend, Bless-ed Je-sus, hold my hand.

CHORUS.

Je - sus, hold my hand, I need...... Thee ev - 'ry
Bless-ed Je - sus, hold my hand, Yes, I need Thee

hour, Thru...... this pil - grim land Pro -
ev - 'ry hour, Thru this land, this pil - grim land

tect me by Thy pow'r; Hear.... my fee-ble plea,
By Thy sav-ing pow'r; Hear my plea, my fee - ble plea,

O Lord,...... look down on me, When I kneel in
Lord, dear Lord, look down on me, When

pray'r I hope to meet you there, Bless-ed Je-sus, hold my hand.
I kneel in pray'r,

167 Look for Me at Jesus' Feet

S. P., Jr.

Squire Parsons, Jr.

1. If I leave ___ this world ___ of sor-row ___ some-time ___ be-fore you do, ___ Just look ___ for me ___ in heav-en ___ and we'll talk ___ the a - ges through; ___ But if, at first, ___ you fail ___ to see me ___ let me tell ___ you where I'll be, ___ I'll be thank - ing Christ, ___ my Sav-ior, ___ for ___ sav-ing a

2. But if you ___ should reach ___ that cit - y ___ be - fore ___ my time has come, ___ Per - haps ___ you'd like ___ to greet me ___ when my race ___ down here is run; ___ Just ___ wait, ___ for I'll soon ___ be com - ing ___ a - cross ___ life's ebb - ing sea, ___ And I'll tell ___ you now, ___ my broth - er, ___ just ___ where ___ to

CHORUS

wretch like me. _____ Don't _ look 'neath the gates of pearl, _____ don't
wait for me. _____ Don't _ wait 'neath the gates of pearl, _____ don't

look on the streets of gold, _____ Don't look by the walls of jas - per, ___
wait on the streets of gold, _____ Don't wait by the walls of jas - per, ___

nor a - mong the man - y sights un - told; _____ For I've been long - ing and
nor a - mong the man - y sights un - told; _____ For I've been long - ing and

I've been wait - ing _____ for the pre - cious, ho - ly One to meet, ___ There I'll
I've been wait - ing _____ for the pre - cious, ho - ly One to meet, ___ There I'll

be through the count-less a - ges, _____ look for me at Je - sus' feet. _____
be through the count-less a - ges, _____ wait for me at Je - sus' feet. _____

168

The Brush

C. M.

Chuck Millhuff
Arr. by Harold Lane

Life started out like a can-vas, __ And God started painting on me, __ But I
took the paint brush from Jesus, and painted what I wished to see; The colors I
paint-ed kept running, __ And the ob-jects were all out of size, __ I had made a mess
of my painting, __ My way now seemed so unwise. Ooo __ Ooo __ So I
brought my painting to Jesus, __ All the col - ors, all the piec-es, so wrong, __ In the

markets of earth it was worthless,—But His blood made my painting belong.— He

worked with no condemnation, Never mentioned the mess I had made, Then He dipped

His brush in the rainbow, And He signed it, "The price has been paid." When I gave the

brush back to Jesus, _____ When I gave the brush back to Him, He start-ed all o-

ver life's can-vas to fill, When I gave to Je-sus, the brush of my will. _

169   Where We'll Never Grow Old

J. C. M.   (To my father and mother.--J. C. M.)   Jas. C. Moore

1. I have heard of a land on the far away strand, 'Tis a beau-ti-ful home of the soul; Built by Je-sus on high, there we nev-er shall die, 'Tis a land where we'll nev-er grow old.
2. In that beau-ti-ful home where we'll nevermore roam, We shall be in that sweet by and by; Hap-py praise to the King thru e-ter-ni-ty sing, 'Tis a land where we nev-er shall die.
3. When our work here is done and our life crown is won, And our troubles and tri-als are o'er; All our sor-row will end, and our voic-es will blend, With the loved ones who've gone on be-fore.

CHORUS

Nev-er grow old, where we'll nev-er grow old, In a land where we'll never grow old; Nev-er grow old, where we'll nev-er grow old, In a land where we'll never grow old.

The Glory Land Way

170

J.S.T.

J. S. Torbett

1. I'm in the way, the bright and shin-ing way, I'm in the glo-ry land
2. List to the call, the gos-pel call to-day, Get in the glo-ry land
3. On-ward I go, re-joic-ing in His love, I'm in the glo-ry land

way;
glo - ry land way;

Tell-ing the world that Je-sus saves to-day, Yes,
Wand'rers, come home, oh, hast-en to o-bey, And
Soon I shall see Him in that home a-bove, Oh,

CHORUS

I'm in the glo-ry land way.
get
I'm

I'm in the glo-ry land
glo - ry land way

way,
glo - ry land way,

i m in in the glo-ry land way;
glo - ry land way;

Heav-en is

near-er, and the way groweth clearer, For I'm in the glo-ry land way.
glo - ry land way.

171 Jesus Is Coming Soon

R. E. W.

R. E. Winsett

1. Trou-ble-some times are here, fill-ing men's hearts
2. Love of so man-y cold, los-ing their home
3. Trou-bles will soon be o'er, hap-py for-ev-

with fear, Freedom we all hold dear now is at stake;.........
of gold, This in God's Word is told, e-vils a-bound,........
er-more; When we meet on that shore, free from all care;.........

Humb'ling your heart to God, saved from the chast-
When these signs come to pass, near-ing the end
Ris-ing up in the sky; tell-ing the world

𝄋

Fine

'ning rod, Seek the way pil-grims trod, Chris-tians, a-wake.
at last, It will come ver-y fast, trum-pets will sound.
good-by, Home-ward we then will fly, glo-ry to share.

D. S.-Heavenward bound.

CHORUS

Je-sus is com-ing soon morn-ing or night
Je-sus is com-ing soon morn-ing or

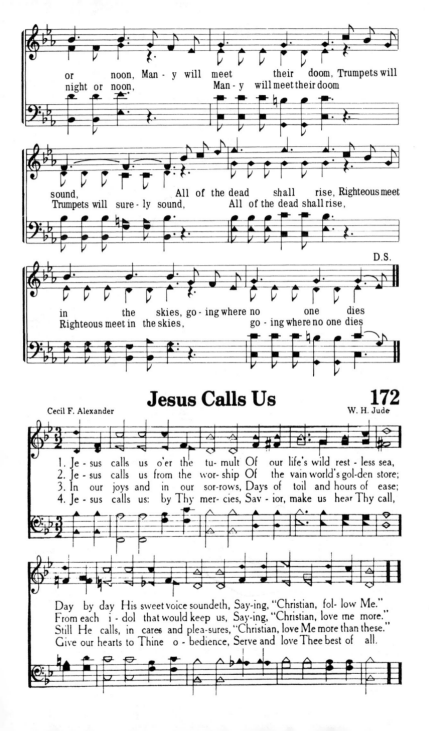

or noon, Man-y will meet their doom, Trumpets will
night or noon, Man-y will meet their doom

sound, All of the dead shall rise, Righteous meet
Trumpets will sure-ly sound, All of the dead shall rise,

D.S.

in the skies, go-ing where no one dies
Righteous meet in the skies, go-ing where no one dies

Jesus Calls Us 172

Cecil F. Alexander   W. H. Jude

1. Je-sus calls us o'er the tu-mult Of our life's wild rest-less sea,
2. Je-sus calls us from the wor-ship Of the vain world's gol-den store;
3. In our joys and in our sor-rows, Days of toil and hours of ease;
4. Je-sus calls us: by Thy mer-cies, Sav-ior, make us hear Thy call,

Day by day His sweet voice soundeth, Say-ing, "Christian, fol-low Me."
From each i-dol that would keep us, Say-ing, "Christian, love me more."
Still He calls, in cares and plea-sures, "Christian, love Me more than these."
Give our hearts to Thine o-bedience, Serve and love Thee best of all.

173 I'll Have a New Life

L. G. P.

Luther G. Presley

1. On the res-ur-rec-tion morn-ing when all the dead in Christ shall rise,
2. Free from ev-'ry im-per-fec-tion, youth-ful and hap-py I shall be,
3. What a hal-le-lu-jah morn-ing when the last trump of God shall sound,

I'll have a new bod-y, Praise the Lord, I'll have a new life; e-ter-nal;

Sown in weak-ness, raised in pow-er, read-y to live in Par-a-dise,
Glo-ri-fied with Him for-ev-er, death will be lost in vic-to-ry,
Graves all burst-ing, saints a shout-ing, heav-en-ly beau-ty all a-round.

I'll have a new bod-y, Praise the Lord I'll have a new life. O yes.

Chorus

Glo-ry, glo-ry, nev-er sad.
I'll have a new home of love e-ter-nal with the re-deemed of God to stand,

There'll be no more sor-row, No more pain, there'll be no more strife; no strife;

Yes, raised in the like-ness of my Sav-ior, read-y to live in glo-ry land, In His like-ness, I'll be glad,

I'll have a new bod-y, Praise the Lord, I'll have a new life. e-ter-nal.

Holy Bible, Book Divine   174

John Burton

Wm. B. Bradbury

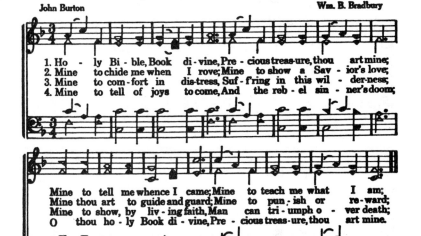

1. Ho - ly Bi - ble, Book di-vine, Pre - cious treas-ure, thou art mine;
2. Mine to chide me when I rove; Mine to show a Sav - ior's love;
3. Mine to com - fort in dis-tress, Suf - f'ring in this wil - der-ness;
4. Mine to tell of joys to come, And the reb - el sin - ner's doom;

Mine to tell me whence I came; Mine to teach me what I am;
Mine thou art to guide and guard; Mine to pun - ish or re-ward;
Mine to show, by liv - ing faith, Man can tri - umph o - ver death;
O thou ho - ly Book di - vine, Pre - cious treas-ure, thou art mine.

175 He Will Pilot Me

Charles T. Bailey

Byron L. Whitworth

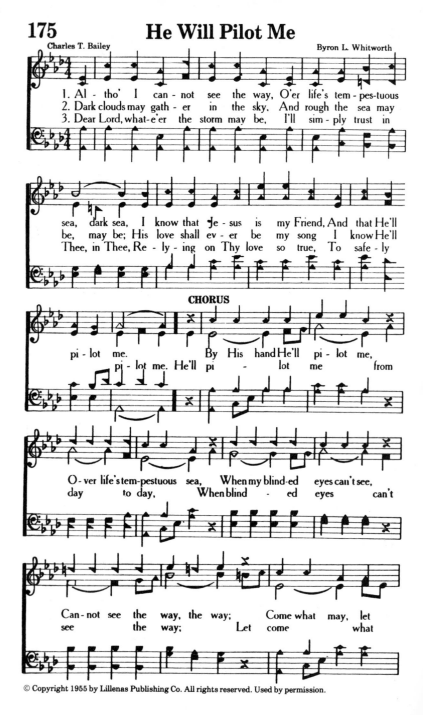

1. Al - tho' I can - not see the way, O'er life's tem - pes-tuous
2. Dark clouds may gath - er in the sky, And rough the sea may
3. Dear Lord, what-e'er the storm may be, I'll sim - ply trust in

sea, dark sea, I know that Je - sus is my Friend, And that He'll
be, may be; His love shall ev - er be my song I know He'll
Thee, in Thee, Re - ly - ing on Thy love so true, To safe - ly

CHORUS

pi - lot me. By His hand He'll pi - lot me,
pi - lot me. He'll pi - lot me from

O - ver life's tem-pestuous sea, When my blind-ed eyes can't see,
day to day, When blind - ed eyes can't

Can - not see the way, the way; Come what may, let
see the way; Let come what

come what may, On life's dark and storm-y sea, My dear Lord,
may on life's dark sea, My bless -

bless - ed Lord, He will pi - lot, pi - lot me.
ed Lord will pi - lot me.

Let the Lower Lights Be Burning 176

Matt. 5: 16.

P. P. Bliss

1. Bright-ly beams our Fa-ther's mer -cy, From His lighthouse ev - er-more,
2. Dark the night of sin has set-tled, Loud the an - gry bil-lows roar;
3. Trim your fee - ble lamp, my broth-er: Some poor sail- or tem-pest-tost,

8
FINE

But to us He gives the keep-ing Of the lights a - long the shore.
Ea - ger eyes are watch-ing, long-ing, For the lights a - long the shore.
Try-ing now to make the har-bor, In the dark-ness may be lost.

D. S.-Some poor faint-ing, strug-gling sea-man You may res - cue, you may save.

CHORUS
D. S.

Let the low - er lights be burn-ing! Send a gleam a-cross the wave!

177 Glory Road

C. C.

Conrad Cook

Is the road you're trav-'ling dark, de-sert-ed, or dim, Is there hope

for to-mor-row? Put your trust in Him. On this glo-ry road I'm

trav-'ling, man-y times I stum-ble on my way, But, praise the Lord, I'll

soon be leav-ing To that land of per-fect peace and end-less day.

CHORUS

I can see _____ the lights of home, _____ I can see _____
I can see the _____ lights of home, I can

178 Just a Little Talk with Jesus

C. D.

Cleavant Derricks

1. I once was lost in sin but Je-sus took me in, And then a lit-tle
2. Sometimes my path seems drear, with-out a ray of cheer, And then a cloud of
3. I may have doubts and fears, my eyes be filled with tears, But Je-sus is a

light from heav-en filled my soul; It bathed my heart in love and wrote my
doubt may hide the light of day; The mists of sin may rise and hide the
friend who watch-es day and night; I go to Him in pray'r, He knows my

name a-bove, And just a lit-tle talk with Je-sus made me whole......
star-ry skies, But just a lit-tle talk with Je-sus clears the way.......
ev-'ry care, And just a lit-tle talk with Je-sus makes it right........

CHORUS

Have a lit-tle talk with Je-sus tell Him all a-bout our
Now let us let us

trou-bles, Hear our faint-est cry an-swer by and by;
He will and He will

Feel a lit-tle pray'r wheel turning, know a lit-tle fire is

Now when you and you

burn-ing, Find a lit-tle talk with Je-sus makes it right.

You will it makes it right.

There Is a Name 179

1. There is a name I love to hear, I love to sing its worth; It sounds like
2. It tells me of a Sav-ior's love, Who died to set me free; It tells me
3. It tells me what my Father hath In store for ev - 'ry day, And tho I
4. It tells of One whose lov-ing heart Can feel my deepest woe, Who in each

CHORUS

mu - sic in mine ear, The sweetest name on earth.
of His precious blood, The sinner's perfect plea. Oh, how I love Je-sus,
tread a darksome path, Yields sunshine all the way.
sor - row bears a part, That none can bear below.

Oh, how I love Je-sus, Oh, how I love Je-sus, Because He first loved me!

180 It's Different Now

Arrangement by David Beatty

1. Once I was lost in sin, I had no peace with-in, To save my
2. I went to church one day to hear them sing and pray, The preach-er
3. Sin's fet-ters held me fast, the dye was al-most cast, My proud and
4. And now my hopes are bright, I praise Him day and night, How He could

wea-ry soul I knew not how; But Je-sus came to me, and
firm-ly plowed the gos-pel plow; He said you must re-pent, so
haugh-ty spir-it would not bow; But just one glimpse of Him, it
change me so I know not how; But praise the Lord it's done, the

by His grace I'm free, down the aisle I went, Now it's dif-f'rent O so dif-f'rent
down the aisle I went, Now it's dif-f'rent O so dif-f'rent
broke the pow'r of sin, yes, it's
vic-t'ry now is won,

now.

CHORUS

It's dif-f'rent now, Since Je-sus saved my
Yes, it's dif-f'rent now,

soul, It's dif-f'rent now, since by His blood I'm
since He saved my soul, Yes, it's dif-frent now,

whole; Old Sa-tan had to flee when Je-sus res-cued me,
by His blood I'm whole; Ah............ ah............

Now it's dif-f'rent, O so dif-f'rent now.
yes, it's so dif-f'rent now.

Did You Think to Pray 181

Mrs. M. A. Kidder

W. O. Perkins

1. Ere you left your room this morning, In the name of
2. When you met with great temptation, Did you think to pray? By His dy - ing
3. When your heart was filled with an-ger, Did you plead for
4. When sore tri-als came up - on you, When your soul was

Christ, our Sav-ior, Did you sue for lov-ing fa - vor, As a shield to-day?
love and mer - it, Did you claim the Ho - ly Spir - it As your guide and stay?
grace, my brother, That you might forgive an - oth - er Who have crossed your way?
bowed in sor - row, Balm of Gil - ead did you bor-row At the gates of day?

D. S.—So, when life seems dark and dreary, Don't forget to pray.

Chorus

D. S.

O how pray-ing rests the wea - ry! Pray'r will change the night to day;

182 The Glove

G. J.

Gordon Jensen

1. Just an emp-ty glove __ ly-ing on the ta-ble __ is my life __ with-out __ the Mas-ter's hand, __ Noth-ing on my own, __ so use-less __ a-lone, __ Lord, fill this will-ing glove __ with Your hand. __

A tool and nothin' more, is the glove that is worn
On a carpenter's or on a surgeon's hand;
And no credit belong to the glove he has on,
When God touches lives with His hand.

CHORUS

Lord, let me be ___ the glove You wear ___ to - day, Use me, Lord, to show some- one You care ___ to - day; This is all ___ I ask, ___ As You per - form ___ Your task, ___ Lord, let me be ___ the glove You wear. ___

183 Just a Little While

E. M. B.

E. M. Bartlett

1. Soon this life will all be o - ver And our pil - grim - age will end,
2. Soon we'll see the light of morn-ing, Then the new day will be - gin,
3. Soon we'll meet a - gain our loved ones And we'll take them by the hand,

Soon we'll take our heav'n-ly jour-ney, Be at home a - gain with friends;
Soon we'll hear the Fa - ther call - ing, "Come, my chil - dren en - ter in;"
Soon we'll press them to our bos - om O - ver in the prom-ised land;

Heav-en's gates are stand-ing o - pen, Wait - ing for our en-trance there,
Then we'll hear a choir of an - gels, Sing - ing out the vic - t'ry song,
Then we'll be at home for-ev - er, Thru-out all e - ter - ni - ty,

Some sweet day we're go - ing o - ver, All the beau-ties there to share.
All our trou-bles will be end - ed And we'll live with heaven's throng.
What a bless - ed, bless - ed morn-ing That e - ter - nal morn will be!

184   Queen of Paradise

D. R.

Dottie Rambo

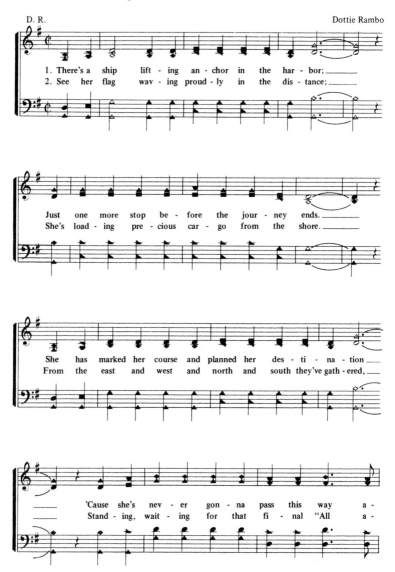

1. There's a ship lift - ing an - chor in the har - bor; ____
2. See her flag wav - ing proud - ly in the dis - tance; ____

Just one more stop be - fore the jour - ney ends. ____
She's load - ing pre - cious car - go from the shore. ____

She has marked her course and planned her des - ti - na - tion ____
From the east and west and north and south they've gath - ered, ____

____ 'Cause she's nev - er gon - na pass this way a -
____ Stand - ing, wait - ing for that fi - nal "All a -

CHORUS

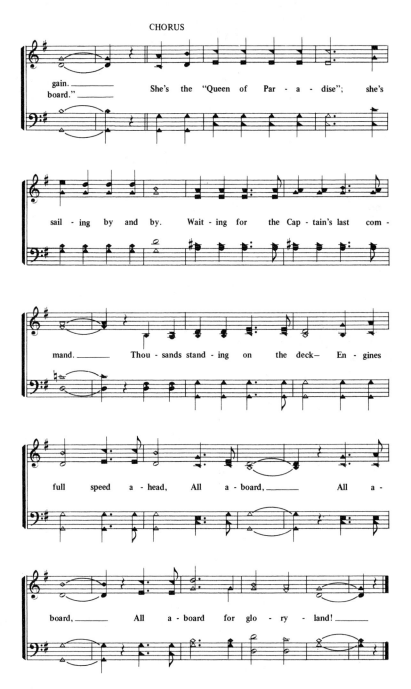

gain. _____
board." _____ She's the "Queen of Par - a - dise"; she's

sail - ing by and by. Wait - ing for the Cap - tain's last com -

mand. _____ Thou - sands stand - ing on the deck— En - gines

full speed a - head, All a - board, _____ All a -

board, _____ All a - board for glo - ry - land! _____

185 I'll Tell the World

(That I'm a Christian)

B. L. F.

Baynard L. Fox

1. I'll tell the world that I'm a Christian— I'm not a-shamed His name to bear; I'll tell the world that I'm a Christian I'll take Him with me an-y-where. I'll tell the world how Je-sus saved me, And how He gave me a life brand-new; And I know that if you trust Him That all He gave me

2. I'll tell the world that He is com-ing— It may be near or far a-way; But we must live as if His com-ing Would be to-mor-row or to-day. For when He comes and life is o-ver, For those who love Him there's more to be; Eyes have nev-er seen the won-ders That He's pre-par-ing

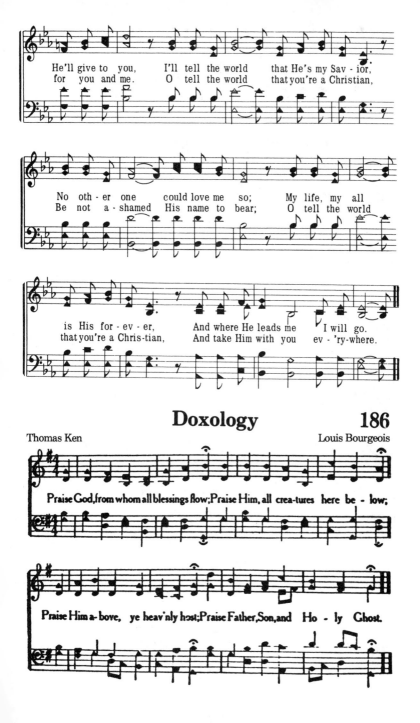

He'll give to you, I'll tell the world that He's my Sav-ior,
for you and me. O tell the world that you're a Christian,

No oth-er one could love me so; My life, my all
Be not a-shamed His name to bear; O tell the world

is His for-ev-er, And where He leads me I will go.
that you're a Chris-tian, And take Him with you ev-'ry-where.

Doxology

186

Thomas Ken

Louis Bourgeois

Praise God, from whom all blessings flow; Praise Him, all crea-tures here be-low;

Praise Him a-bove, ye heav'nly host; Praise Father, Son, and Ho-ly Ghost.

187 Looking for a City

W. Oliver Cooper

Marvin P. Dalton

1. Here a-mong the shad-ows (liv - ing) in a lone-ly land, With strang-ers
2. Here in dis - ap-point-ment(oft-en) we so sad - ly roam, And earth-ly
3. In this land of dan-gers (we are) go - ing here and there, We're sim - ply

we're a band of pil - grims on the move; Thru dan-gers bur - dened
friends no long - er speak one word of love; But tru - ly we have
trust - ing in the bless - ed Sav-ior's love; And mer - cy tho' we

down with sor-rows, And we're shunned on ev - 'ry hand, But we are look-ing
found con-tent-ment, Je - sus prom-ised us a home, So we are look-ing
may be strang-ers, Liv - ing in this world of care, We're al-ways look-ing

CHORUS

for a cit - y built a-bove.
a - bove. O yes we're look-ing here and there Look - -

ing for a cit - y, Where we'll nev - er
Look-ing for a cit - y, Yon-der where we'll nev-er die,

die,   There   the saint-ed mil-lions,
nev-er die no nev-er, And up there with all the saints,   yes, with all the mil-lions,

Nev   ·   er say good-by,
We will   nev-er say good-by,   say good-by no nev-er, Yes and

There   we'll meet our Sav-ior,   And
when we gath-er there,   We'll meet Christ our Sav-ior, Glo-ry and we know we'll meet

our loved ones too,   Come   O ho-ly
friends and, all our loved ones, Now we pray Thee quick-ly come,

Spir · it,   All   our hopes re · new.
Pray Thee come O spir - it, Come O come! on Thee we call,   All our hopes re - new.

188   The Carpenter from Nazareth

J. H., Jr.

Joel Hemphill, Jr.

1. Jesus, our Lord and Savior, was a carpenter by trade; And even though He was the Son of God, He worked 'til He went away: And as He ascended those around Him heard Him say, "I'll prepare a place and come again and take you home to stay."

You might have the finest home there is in the land,
And the worldly goods that you own might be the envy of ev'ry man;
But all of this will pass away and the only thing that will stand
Is what the Carpenter from Naz'reth has built in Gloryland!

CHORUS

For two thou-sand years He's been a work-in' on a place where we will live ___ e-ter-nal-ly; Words can't ex-plain, minds can't con-tain what's wait-ing there for me! ___ The world might own great man-sions, but He holds the world in His hands; And the Car-pen-ter ___ from Naz-'reth built me a home in Glo-ry-land! ___

189 When that Old Ship of Zion
Sails in Home

Jack Clark

J. C.

1. Sail - ing o'er life's _____ o - cean through the storm
2. In my mind I can see her, _____ a once

and the tem - pest, Mind - ing not, though the rag - ing
gray - haired moth - er, Wait - ing there, old and fee -

bil - lows roar; _____ 'Tis the old Ship of Zi - on,
ble no more; _____ Young and strong there she's stand - ing

sails un - furled, ban - ners fly - in', On her jour - ney to
at the foot of the land - ing, There to wel - come her

CHORUS

heav - en's bliss - ful shore. _____ When that old ship of
chil - dren to that shore. _____

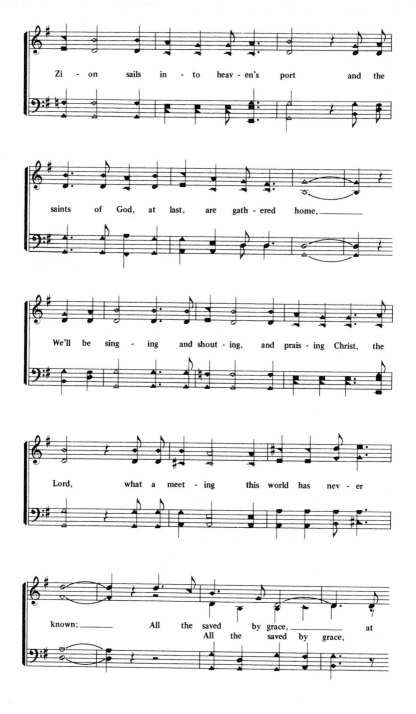

Zi - on sails in - to heav - en's port and the

saints of God, at last, are gath - ered home, _____

We'll be sing - ing and shout - ing, and prais - ing Christ, the

Lord, what a meet - ing this world has nev - er

known; _____ All the saved by grace, _____ at
All the saved by grace,

Somebody Loves Me

190

W. F. C.

W. F. & Marjorie Crumley

1. I'm in love with my Sav-ior and He's in love with me, He is with me from
2. You'll be hap-py if you will let Je - sus have His way, He has work for us
3. Then at last when our work is done, He will call us home To a man-sion He

day to day, What a friend is He; Watch-es o - ver me while I sleep,
all to do Ev - 'ry pass-ing day; Feed the hun - gry and cheer the sad,
has pre-pared Nev- er more to roam, We'll sit down by the riv - er-side,

Hears me when I pray, I am hap-py as I can be, And I now can say:
For the sin- ner, pray. You'll have joy that you nev-er had, And you then can say:
Cares all passed a-way, And with nev- er a pain to bear, What a hap-py day.

D.S. - That some-bod-y is Je-sus, and I know He's mine.

CHORUS

Some - bod - y loves me, an-swers my prayer, I love some-bod - y,

I know He cares; Some - bod - y tells me not to re - pine,

D.S.

191 Touching Jesus

J. S.

John Stallings

Cue Notes for 2nd verse solo

1. A wom-an tried man-y phy-si-cians,
2. I was bound when I knelt at that old al-tar,

Yet grew worse, so to Je-sus she came;
But they said Je-sus could meet ev-'ry need;

And when the crowd tried to restrain her,
And when this pris-'ner fin-'ly touched Je-sus,

She whis-pered these words thro' her pain:
He set me free, praise the Lord, free in-deed!

CHORUS

"Touch-ing Je-sus is all that mat-ters,"

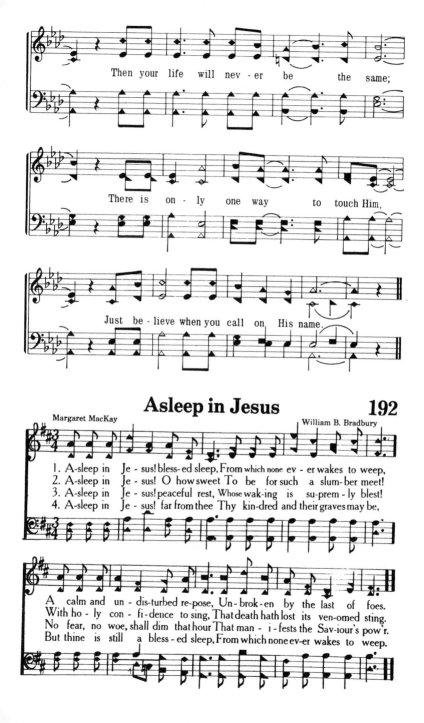

Then your life will nev-er be the same;

There is on-ly one way to touch Him,

Just be-lieve when you call on His name.

Asleep in Jesus

192

Margaret MacKay

William B. Bradbury

1. A-sleep in Je-sus! bless-ed sleep, From which none ev-er wakes to weep,
2. A-sleep in Je-sus! O how sweet To be for such a slum-ber meet!
3. A-sleep in Je-sus! peaceful rest, Whose wak-ing is su-prem-ly blest!
4. A-sleep in Je-sus! far from thee Thy kin-dred and their graves may be,

A calm and un-dis-turbed re-pose, Un-brok-en by the last of foes.
With ho-ly con-fi-dence to sing, That death hath lost its ven-omed sting.
No fear, no woe, shall dim that hour That man-i-fests the Sav-iour's pow'r.
But thine is still a bless-ed sleep, From which none ev-er wakes to weep.

193   Without a Doubt I'm Saved

J. H.

Joel Hemphill

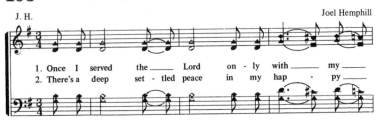

1. Once I served the ____ Lord on - ly with ____ my ____
2. There's a deep set - tled peace in my hap - py ____

lips, And I put ____ my ____ trust in my church ____ mem-ber-
soul, Now my life ____ has an aim, heav - en is ____ my ____

ship; But then my soul had a stir, and I
goal; ____ And the world's gath - 'ring storms can't ____

ear - nest - ly prayed, Till I knew with - out a
make ____ me a - fraid, I can shout "With - out a

CHORUS

doubt _____ I was saved. _____
doubt _____ I'm _____ saved!" _____ With - out a doubt I'm

saved; I've been born _____ a - gain, Washed in Cal - v'ry's

flow, pure and white _____ with - in; Oh, I

once was lost, by sins chains _____ en - slaved, But now I

know with - out a doubt _____ I'm saved! _____

194 I've Got that Old Time Religion in My Heart

H. M.

Hurdist Milsap

1. I'm glad Jesus came, glory to His name, O what a friend is He;
2. What a joy to know One who loves us so, He is so kind and true;
3. Sinner won't you now humbly to Him bow, Just let the Lord come in;

He so freely gave His own life to save, From bonds of sin set free.
He has changed my life from all sin and strife, He'll do the same for you.
You'll find perfect peace, joy will never cease, You shall the life-crown win.

Chorus

I've got that pure love in my heart,
I've got that old time religion in my heart, A

It is now way down inside, I've got that new peace
way down inside, I've got a new kind of feeling in my

in my heart, Where true joys will e'er abide; Nobody knows what is
heart, True joys abide;

means to me, No-bod-y knows but my Lord and me, I've got that
I've got that old

pure love in my heart, It is now way down inside.
time re-li-gion in my heart, A way down in-side.

Close to Thee

195

Fanny J. Crosby

Silas J. Vail

1. Thou, my ev-er-last-ing por-tion, More than friend or life to me;
2. Not for ease or world-ly pleas-ure, Nor for fame my prayer shall be;
3. Lead me through the vale of shad-ows, Bear me o'er life's fit-ful sea;

Fine

D.S.-All a-long my pil-grim jour-ney, Sav-ior, let me walk with Thee.
D.S.-Glad-ly will I toil and suf-fer, On-ly let me walk with Thee.
D.S.-Then the gate of life e-ter-nal May I en-ter, Lord, with Thee.

CHORUS

D.S.

Close to Thee, close to Thee, Close to Thee, close to Thee;

196 There's Coming a Day

W. E. M.

W. Elmo Mercer

1. There's coming a day in God's tomorrow, When trials are past and heaven's in view. No burdens to bear, no tears of sorrow, For God will be
near to car-ry me through. The gates will o-pen and I shall enter
My home for-ev - er with Him to stay. What glo-ry 'twill be when I see
Je - sus, My won-der - ful Lord, There's com-ing a day.

2. The dawning will come and I'll see Je-sus Just waiting for me on heaven's bright shore. I'll rush to His side and say, "Dear Master, I'm coming back
home to wander no more." O bliss-ful moment on yonder portals,
I'll praise my Je-sus, the Truth, the Way. Till then I will be a happy
pil-grim, My jour - ney will end, There's com-ing a day.

The Unseen Hand

197

A. J. S.

A. J. Sims

1. There is an un- seen Hand to me ___ That leads thru ways ___
2. His hand has led ___ thru shadows drear ___ And while it leads ___
3. I long to see ___ my Sav-ior's face ___ And sing the sto -

I can-not see ___ While go - ing thru ___ this world of woe ___
I have no fear ___ I know 'twill lead ___ me to that home ___
ry saved by grace ___ And there up - on ___ that gold-en strand ___

CHORUS

This hand still leads ___ me as I go. ___
Where sin nor sor -rows e'er can come. ___ I'm trusting to ___ the unseen
I'll praise Him for ___ His guid-ing hand. ___

hand ___ That guides me thru ___ this wear-y land ___ And some sweet

day ___ I'll reach that strand ___ Still guid-ed by ___ the unseen hand. ___

198 The Master of the Sea

S. P., Jr.

Squire Parsons, Jr.

1. One ___ night up - on ___ the sea, ___ a ship was toss - ing
2. Though the storms of life ___ may rage ___ and the bil - lows

to and fro, ___ Break - ers dashed on ev - 'ry hand, ___
'round you roll, ___ He can calm life's trou - bled sea ___

an - gry winds a - round did blow; ___ All on board were
as He did in days of old; ___ As up - on life's

filled ___ with fright ___ as the might - y bil - lows rolled, ___
sea ___ you sail, ___ trust in Him who nev - er fails. ___

Then they called up - on the one ___ who the winds and waves con -
I'm so glad He sails with me, ___ He's the Mas - ter of the

CHORUS

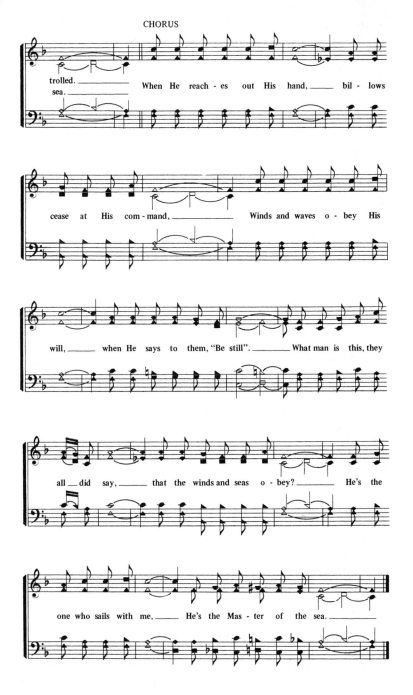

trolled. _____
sea. _____ When He reach - es out His hand, _____ bil - lows

cease at His com - mand, _____ Winds and waves o - bey His

will, _____ when He says to them, "Be still". _____ What man is this, they

all __ did say, _____ that the winds and seas o - bey? _____ He's the

one who sails with me, _____ He's the Mas - ter of the sea. _____

199 Is My Lord Satisfied with Me?

E. W. S.

E. W. (Bill) Suggs

1. One glo-r'ous day Je-sus came and made me whole, He so com-
2. I'm sat-is-fied with God's great re-demp-tion plan I'm sat-is-
3. Lord give me strength, give me cour-age, make me bold That I might

plete-ly then sat-is-fied my soul; Now as I face life's dark trou-bled
fied it's suf-fi-cient all for man; I'm sat-is-fied with His work on
lead some lost sheep in-to Thy fold; That I might stand un-a-fraid un-

storm-y sea, I won-der if He is sat-is-fied with me?
Cal-va-ry, But is my Lord ful-ly sat-is-fied with me?
moved for Thee, That you might be ful-ly sat-is-fied with me.

CHORUS

I want my Lord to be sat-is-fied with me: I want my life to

be what He'd have it be; Then when I come to that great e-ter-ni-

ty, His smile will say He is sat-is-fied with me

sat-is-fied with me.

O Worship the King

200

Robert Grant

Johann M. Haydn

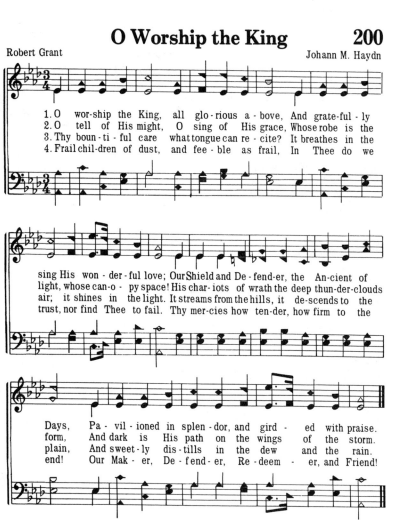

1. O wor-ship the King, all glo-rious a-bove, And grate-ful-ly sing His won-der-ful love; Our Shield and De-fend-er, the An-cient of Days, Pa-vil-ioned in splen-dor, and gird-ed with praise.

2. O tell of His might, O sing of His grace, Whose robe is the light, whose can-o-py space! His char-iots of wrath the deep thun-der-clouds form, And dark is His path on the wings of the storm.

3. Thy boun-ti-ful care what tongue can re-cite? It breathes in the air; it shines in the light. It streams from the hills, it de-scends to the plain, And sweet-ly dis-tills in the dew and the rain.

4. Frail chil-dren of dust, and fee-ble as frail, In Thee do we trust, nor find Thee to fail. Thy mer-cies how ten-der, how firm to the end! Our Mak-er, De-fend-er, Re-deem-er, and Friend!

201   The Eastern Gate

Arr. by W. Elmo Mercer

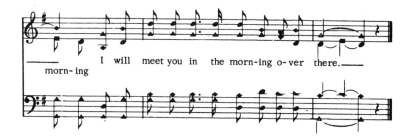

morn-ing

I will meet you in the morn-ing o-ver there.

Sweet Hour of Prayer 202

W. W. Walford

Wm. B. Bradbury

1. Sweet hour of pray'r, sweet hour of pray'r, That calls me from a world of care,
2. Sweet hour of pray'r, sweet hour of pray'r, The joys I feel, the bliss I share,
3. Sweet hour of pray'r, sweet hour of pray'r, Thy wings shall my pe - ti - tion bear

And bids me, at my Father's throne, Make all my wants and wish-es known!
Of those whose anx-ious spir-its burn With strong de-sires for thy re-turn!
To Him, whose truth and faithfulness En-gage the wait-ing' soul to bless:

Fine

D. S.—And oft es-capes the tempter's snare By the re-turn, sweet hour of pray'r.
D. S.—And glad-ly take my sta - tion there, And wait for thee, sweet hour of pray'r.
D. S.—I'll cast on Him my ev - 'ry care, And wait for thee, sweet hour of pray'r.

D.S.

In sea - sons of dis - tress and grief, My soul has oft - en found re - lief,
With such I has - ten to the place, Where God, my Savior, shows His face,
And since He bids me seek His face, Be-lieve His word, and trust His grace,

203 He's with Me Always

C. W.

Clarence Williams

1. From the light of ear - ly morn - ing till the eve - ning
2. He is with me when I'm sing - ing; when I'm lone - ly,
3. Now I'm sing - ing on the moun - tain and the bless - ings

sha - dows fall, And the lone - ly mid - night reach - es in - to
He is near; In the sun - shine or the rain, He's al - ways
flood my soul; ___ ___ God is there to share my ev - 'ry

dawn. ___ ___ ___ Ev - 'ry liv - ing mo - ment, ev - 'ry
there. ___ ___ ___ An - y - where I go, ___ an - y -
song. ___ When I'm walk - ing through the val - ley, when the

breath of life I ___ take, Oh, it's good to know, ___
thing that comes my ___ way, It's so good to know, ___
sha - dows cross my ___ way, Yes, it's good to know, ___

CHORUS

Lo, He's with me al -- ways. _____
God is with me al - ways. _____ Al - ways, to-
Lo, He's with me al - ways. _____

day, to - mor - row, Al - ways, in joy or sor - row,

I know, Lo, He's with me al - ways. _____

Al - ways, and for - ev - er, Al - ways, He will

nev - er leave me, God is with me al - ways. _____

204 Sorry, I Never Knew You

Henkle M. Little
Arr. by Jeffie Steele

Sherman Branch

1. Last night as I was sleep-ing, this dream came to me; I
2. I thought the time had come when I must stand the trial, I
3. There was my wife and chil-dren, I heard each one's voice, They
4. When I from sleep a-wak-ened, with tears in my eyes, I

dreamed a-bout the end of time a-bout e-ter-ni-ty; I
told the Lord that I had been a Chris-tian all the while; But
must have all been hap - py, it seemed they did re-joice, With
looked, a-round, and there a-bout me, to my great sur-prise, I

saw a mil-lion sin-ners fall on their faces to pray, The Sav-ior
through the book He then looked, and sad-ly shook His head; They placed me
robes of white a-round them, and crowns up-on their head; My lit-tle
saw my wife and ba-bies, and knew I'd had a dream, Then down be-

CHORUS

sad-ly shook His head, and this I heard him say; Sor-ry, I ne-ver
o-ver on His left, and this is what He said; Sor-ry, I ne-ver
girl looked up at me, and this is what she said; Dad-dy, we can't go
side my bed I fell, and for mer-cy did scream; Fa-ther, Who art in

knew you, de-part from me for ev-er more; Sor-ry, I
knew you, I find no re-cord of your birth; Sor-ry, I
with you, We must stay on this love-ly shore; Sor-ry, for
glo-ry, In mer-cy look on me to-day; For-give me

© Copyright 1957 by Faith Music Co. All rights reserved. Used by permission.

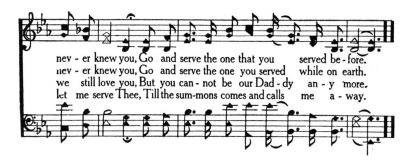

nev - er knew you, Go and serve the one that you served be-fore.
nev - er knew you, Go and serve the one you served while on earth.
we still love you, But you can - not be our Dad - dy an - y more.
let me serve Thee, Till the sum-mons comes and calls me a - way.

We'll Work Till Jesus Comes 205

Elizabeth Mills

William Miller

1. O land of rest, for thee I sigh! When will the mo-ment come When
2. To Je - sus Christ I fled for rest! He bade me cease to roam, And
3. I sought at once my Sav - ior's side, No more my steps shall roam, With

CHORUS

I shall lay my ar - mor by, And dwell in peace at home? We'll work till
lean for suc-cor on His breast Till He conducts me home.
Him I'll brave death's chilling tide, And reach my Heav'nly home. We'll work

Je - sus comes, We'll work till Je-sus comes; And we'll be gathered home.
We'll work

206   We Will Rise and Shine

S. E. L.

Arr. J. T. B. Pub. Co.

1. We are climbing Jacob's ladder, ladder, We are climbing
   We are climbing   *We are climbing*
2. Each day brings me one round higher, higher, Each day brings me
3. Je-sus cleanseth all who trust Him, trust Him, Je-sus cleanseth
4. Don't you wish you had this blessing, blessing, Don't you wish you
5. Je-sus died that you might have it, have it, Jesus died that

Jacob's ladder, ladder, We are climbing Jacob's ladder, ladder,
   We are climbing
one round higher, higher, Each day brings me one round higher, higher,
all who trust Him, trust Him, Je-sus cleanseth all who trust Him, trust Him,
had this blessing, blessing, Don't you wish you had this blessing, blessing,
you might have it, have it, Je-sus died that you might have it, have it,

CHORUS.

sol-diers of the cross. We will rise and shine, and give God the
   rise and   *shine and*

glo-ry, glo-ry, Rise and shine and give God the glo-ry, glo-ry,
   rise and   *shine and*

Rise and shine and give God the glory, glory, Soldiers of the cross.
   rise and   *shine and*

Were You There?

207

Arranged for John T. Benson Publishing Co.

1. Were you there when they cru - ci - fied my Lord? (were you there?)
2. Were you there when they nailed Him to the tree? (to the tree?)
3. Were you there when they pierced Him in the side? (in the side?)
4. Were you there when the sun re - fused to shine? (were you there?)
5. Were you there when they laid Him in the tomb? (in the tomb?)

Were you there when they cru - ci - fied my Lord? Oh! . . . .
Were you there when they nailed Him to the tree? Oh! . . . .
Were you there when they pierced Him in the side? Oh! . . . .
Were you there when the sun re - fused to shine? Oh! . . . .
Were you there when they laid Him in the tomb? Oh! . . . .

Some - times it caus - es me to trem - ble, trem - ble,
Some - times it caus - es me to trem - ble, trem - ble,
Some - times it caus - es me to trem - ble, trem - ble,
Some - times it caus - es me to trem - ble, trem - ble,
Some - times it caus - es me to trem - ble, trem - ble,

trem - ble, Were you there when they cru - ci - fied my Lord?
trem - ble, Were you there when they nailed Him to the tree?
trem - ble, Were you there when they pierced Him in the side?
trem - ble, Were you there when the sun re - fused to shine?
trem - ble, Were you there when they laid Him in the tomb?

208 Just a Closer Walk with Thee

Anonymous

Arr. for John T. Benson, Jr.

1. I am weak but Thou art strong (Thou art strong), Je-sus keep me from all
2. Thru this world of toil and snares (toil and snares), If I fal-ter, Lord, who
3. When my fee-ble life is o'er (life is o'er), Time for me will be no

wrong (from all wrong); I'll be sat-is-fied as long (just as long), As I walk let me
cares (Lord, who cares)? Who with me my burden shares (burden shares)? None but Thee, dear
more (be no more); Guide me gently, safely o'er (safely o'er), To Thy king-dom

CHORUS.

walk close to Thee (close to Thee).
Lord, none but Thee (none but Thee).   Just a closer walk with Thee (walk with Thee),
shore, to Thy shore (to Thy shore).

Grant it, Je-sus, is my plea (hum-ble plea); Dai-ly walk-ing close to

Thee (close to Thee), Let it be, dear Lord, let it be (let it be).

Kneel at the Cross

209

Words and Melody by Charles E. Moody

Arr. for John T. Benson, Jr.

1. Kneel at the cross, Christ will meet you there, Come while He waits for you;
2. Kneel at the cross, There is room for all Who would His glo - ry share;
3. Kneel at the cross, Give your i - dols up, Look un - to realms a - bove;

List to His voice, Leave with Him your care And be - gin life a - new
Bliss there a-waits, Harm can ne'er be-fall Those who are anchored there.
Turn not a - way To life's sparkling cup, Trust on - ly in His love.

Chorus

Kneel.......... .... at the cross,............Leave............
Kneel at the cross, Kneel at the cross, Leave ev-'ry care

ev - 'ry care;......... ..... Kneel............... at the
Leave ev - 'ry care; Kneel at the cross,

cross.............. Je - sus will meet you there............
Kneel at the cross, meet you there.

210   I'm in this Church

J. H.

Joel Hemphill

CHORUS

I'm in this church, this glo-ri-ous church;

I did-n't join, Oh I was born, I've had a new

birth! Some glo-ri-ous day, gon-na sail a-

way; _____ It's by His grace, not by my

Last time to

VERSE

works I'm in this church! ___ When Je-sus came,

211 Caught Up Together

R. L. H.

Roger L. Horne

1. There soon will come a day and hour though no man know-eth
2. When Je - sus comes that fi - nal morn we'll hear the trum - pet

when, Our Christ, our Lord and Mas - ter will come back to earth a -
blast, Sweet mu - sic to the Chris - tian's ear we'll know He's come at

gain; The Bi - ble tells us how the dead in Christ shall rise that
last; Don't look for me, I'll not be found, I'm go - ing up with

day, Then with that might - y glo - rious host my soul shall fly a - way.
Him, I'll take my trip on Zi - on's ship, to Heav - en's pier sail in.

CHORUS

212 The Old Account Settled Long Ago

F. M. G.

F. M. Graham
Arranged John T. Benson, Jr.

1. There was a time I know, When in the book of heav'n, An old ac-count
2. The old ac-count was large, And larger ev-'ry day, For I was al
3. When at the judgment bar, I stand be-fore my King, And He the book
4. O sin-ner seek the Lord, Re-pent of all your sin, For thus He has

was stand-ing, For sins yet un - for-giv'n; My name was at the top,
ways sin-ning, And nev - er tried to pay; But when I looked a - head,
will o - pen, And can-not find a thing; Then my heart will be glad,
com-mand-ed, If you would en - ter in; And then if you should live,

And man - y things be - low, But I went to the keep - er, And
And saw such pain and woe, I said that I would set - tle, And
While tears of joy will flow, Be - cause I had it set - tled, And
A hun - dred years be - low, Up there you'll not re - gret it, You

CHORUS

set - tled long a - go. Long a - go, long a-
Down on my knees,

go, yes, the old ac-count was set - tled long
I set - tled it all.

a - go, And the rec-ord's clear to-day, For He

Hal - le - lu - jah!

washed my sin's a-way, When the old ac-count was set-tled long a - go.

Jesus Loves Me   213

Anna B. Warner   Wm. B. Bradbury

1. Je - sus loves me! this I know, For the Bi - ble tells me so; Lit - tle
2. Je - sus loves me! He who died, Heaven's gates to o - pen wide; He will
3. Je - sus loves me! loves me still, Tho' I'm ver - y weak and ill; From His

CHORUS

ones to Him be - long, They are weak but He is strong.
wash a - way my sin, Let His lit - tle child come in. Yes, Je-sus loves me,
shin-ing throne on high, Comes to watch me where I lie.

Yes, Je - sus loves me. Yes, Je-sus loves me, The Bi - ble tells me so.

214   The Old Gospel Ship

Arr. Alphus LeFevre

1. I have good news to bring and that is why I sing, All my joys with you
2. O I can scarcely wait I know I'll not be late, For I'll spend my time
3. If you're ashamed of me you have no cause to be, For with Christ I am

I'll share;   I'm going to take a trip in the Old   Gos - pel ship
in pray'r;   And when my ship comes in   I will leave this world of sin
an heir;   If too much fault you find you will sure be left behind

CHORUS

And   go sail - ing thru the air.
And   go sail - ing thru the air.   O I'm "gon-na" take a trip, in the
While I   go sail - ing thru the air.

good Old Gos-pel Ship, I'm go - ing far beyond the sky;   O I'm "gon-na"

shout and sing un-til the heavens ring, When I'm bidding this world good-by.

The Fire Song

215

Unknown

Arr. by Mrs. James Pate

1. Oh, the judg-ment day is com-ing; What an aw-ful day'twill be!
2. At the sound-ing of the trump-et, At the dawning of the day,
3. Poor lost sin-ners will be cry-ing For that home they'll nev-er see,

Christ for-ev-er is my ref-uge, "Rock of A-ges, cleft for me"
World-ly pleas-ures with their treas-ures Shall for-ev-er pass a-way.
But the ran-somed will be sing-ing, "Rock of Ag-es, cleft for me."

CHORUS

Oh, my lov-ing *bro-ther, when the world's on fi-re, Don't you

want God's bos-om for to be your pil-low? Hide me o-ver in the

Rock of A-ges: "Rock of A-ges, cleft for me."

*May also use "Sister," "Deacon," "Pastor," "Mourner," etc.

216 When My Feet Touch the Streets of Gold

C. C.

Conrad Cook

1. I am look - ing for the day when I'll see
2. If, by chance, some hap - py morn - ing you should

Je - sus,   And His bless - ed face I shall be -
miss me,   Don't you weep for me be - cause I'm

hold;   With the saints of old, ___ the
gone;   I'll be at the feet of the

half will then be told, When my feet touch the
one who died for me, When my feet touch the

CHORUS

streets of gold.   When my feet touch the streets of
streets of gold.

glo - ry, When I've trav - eled my last wea - ry

mile; Will He hold my trem - bling hand when be -
Will He hold my trem - bling hand

fore the bar I stand, Will He say, "My child, well
when be - fore the bar I stand, Will He say, "My

done, a crown of life you now have
child, well done, a crown of life have you've

won", When my feet touch the streets of gold?
won",

217 When the Saints Go Marching in

Verses by John T. Benson, Jr.
Chorus traditional

Arr. by H. F. Hammond

1. I'm a pil-grim and a stran-ger Wan-d'ring thro' this world of sin,
2. Oh, I know I'll see my Sav-iour If my life is free from sin,
3. When we gath-er 'round the Throne And the gates are closed with-in,
4. I'm wait-ing for the char-iot To swing low and I'll step in.

On my way to that fair cit-y, When the Saints go marching in.
Heav-en's doors will o-pen for me When the Saints go marching in.
I'll be shout-ing "Glo-ry, Glo-ry" When the Saints go marching in.
On the clouds I'll ride to Heav-en When the Saints go marching in;

CHORUS

When the saints go marching in, When the saints go
When the saints marching in, Saints go

march - ing in; Lord I want to be in that
march - ing in go march-ing in O

num-ber When the saints go march-ing in.
that num-ber, Saints go march-ing in go march-ing in,

count - less num-ber,

Everytime I Feel the Spirit   218

Verses John T. Benson, Jr.
Chorus traditional

Arr. by H. F. Hammond

CHORUS

O ev-'ry time I feel the spir-it, mov-ing in my heart I will pray;

Oh, ev-'ry time I feel the spir-it mov-ing In my heart I will pray,

Verses

Oh ev-'ry pray 1. Up-on the moun-tain thro val-ley deep, the spir-its
2. Some peo-ple wor-ry and some com-plain, the way they

with me to al-ways keep If dark-ness hides me I can-not stray
grum-ble it is a shame I try to tell them a bet-ter way

Optional ending
D. C.

The spir-it leads me right in the way. Mov-ing my in heart I will pray
A-bout the spir-it and how to pray.

219 This Is Just What Heaven Means to Me

Arr. by W. Elmo Mercer

1. A coun-try where no twilight shadows deep-en, —— Un-end-ing
2. A place where there is no misun-der- stand-ing, —— And from all
3. And when at last we see the face of Je - sus, —— Be- fore whose

day where night will nev - er be; —— A cit - y where the
en-mi- ty and strife we're free; —— No un-kind words to
im-age oth- er loves all flee; —— And when they crown Him

storm clouds can-not gath-er, —— Oh,
wound the heart are —— spok-en, —— Now this is just what heav-en means to
Lord of all I'll —— be there, For

CHORUS

me! —— What joy 'twill be when we get o-ver yon-der, —— And

join the throng a - round the crys-tal sea! —— To meet our loved ones

and crown Christ forever,___ Oh, this is just what heaven means to me!___

Higher Ground

220

Johnson Oatman, Jr.

Charles H. Gabriel

1. I'm press-ing on the up-ward way. New heights I'm gain-ing ev-'ry
2. My heart has no de-sire to stay Where doubts a-rise and fears dis-
3. I want to scale the ut-most height, And catch a gleam of glo-ry

day; Still pray-ing as I'm onward bound, "Lord, plant my feet on higher ground."
may; Tho' some may dwell where these abound, My prayer, my aim, is high-er ground.
bright; But still I'il pray till heav'n I've found, "Lord, lead me on to higher ground."

CHORUS

Lord, lift me up and let me stand, By faith, on heav-en's ta-ble

land, A high-er plane than I have found; Lord, plant my feet on high-er ground.

221 Yes, I Know

Mrs. A. W. W.

Mrs. Anna W. Waterman

1. Come, ye sin - - - ners, lost and hope - - less, Je-sus'
   Come, ye sin-ners, lost and hopeless, lost and hopeless,
2. To the faint He giv - eth pow - - er, Thro' the
   To the faint He giv - eth pow-er, giv - eth pow-er,
3. In temp-ta - tion He is near thee, Holds the
   In temp-ta-tion He is near thee, He is near thee,
4. He will keep thee while the a - ges Roll thro'
   He will keep thee while the a-ges, while the a-ges,

blood can make you free; For He saved the worst a-
Jesus' blood can make you free, can make you free: For He saved the worst a-
moun - tains makes a way; Find-eth wa - ter in the
Thro' the mountains makes a way, He makes a way; Find-eth water in the
pow'rs of hell at bay; Guides you to the path of
Holds the pow'rs of hell at bay, of hell at bay; Guides you to the path of
out e - ter-ni - ty; Tho' earth hin - ders and hell
Roll thro'-out e - ter-ni - ty, e - ter-ni - ty; Tho' earth hinders and hell

mong you, When He saved a wretch like me.
mong you, worst among you, When He saved a wretch like me, a wretch like me.
des - ert, Turns the night to gold-en day.
des - ert, in the desert, Turns the night to gold-en day, to golden day.
safe - ty, Gives you grace for ev-'ry day.
safe-ty, path of safety, Gives you grace for ev-'ry day, for ev-'ry day.
rag - es, All must work for good to thee.
rag - es, and hell rages, All must work for good to thee, for good to thee.

CHORUS.

And I know, yes, I know, Je-sus'
I sure - ly know, I sure - ly know,

blood can make the vil-est sin-ner clean. clean.

vil - est sin-ner clean. vil - est sin-ner clean.

There Is a Fountain 222

William Cowper

Lowell Mason

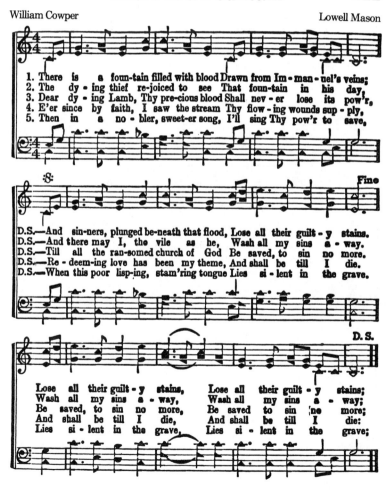

1. There is   a foun-tain filled with blood Drawn from Im-man-uel's veins;
2. The   dy - ing thief re-joiced to   see That foun-tain   in   his   day,
3. Dear dy - ing Lamb, Thy pre-cious blood Shall nev - er lose   its pow'r,
4. E'er since by faith, I saw the stream Thy flow - ing wounds sup - ply,
5. Then   in   a   no - bler, sweet-er song, I'll sing Thy pow'r to   save,

D.S.—And   sin-ners, plunged be-neath that flood, Lose all   their guilt - y stains.
D.S.—And there may I, the   vile   as   he, Wash all   my sins   a - way.
D.S.—Till   all   the ran-somed church of God Be saved, to   sin   no more.
D.S.—Re - deem-ing love has been my theme, And shall be till   I   die.
D.S.—When this poor lisp-ing, stam'ring tongue Lies si - lent in   the grave.

Lose all   their guilt - y stains,   Lose all   their guilt - y stains;
Wash all   my sins   a - way,   Wash all   my sins   a - way;
Be saved, to sin   no   more,   Be saved to   sin no   more;
And shall be till I   die,   And shall be till I   die:
Lies si - lent in the grave,   Lies si - lent in the grave;

223 Neither Do I Condemn Thee

Arr. C. S. & J. S.

Arr. by Carol Snow & Jimmy Snow

1. By the crowd of wor-ship-pers, Sor - ry for their sins, Was a poor
2. They told of her wan-der-ings, Mak - ing each flaw, Spoke of her
3. Still cried the Phar-i - sees, "Pray, Mas-ter, pray, What shall we
4. Cheeks flush-ing with the shame, Turn - ing a - bout, And from His
5. Spoke He most ten-der-ly, "Pray, wom-an, pray, Hast Thou no ac-

wan - der - er, Rude - ly brought in; Scribes came and Phar-i - sees,
pun - ishment, Quot - ing the law; Writ - ing up - on the ground,
do with her? What doth Thou Say?" Then said He re - buk-ing - ly,
pres - ence, Walk-ing slow - ly out. Then saw we stand-ing there,
cu - sers?" "Nay, Mas - ter, nay," "Neither do I con-demn thee,

Anx-ious to see What the meek Naz - a - rene's Ver - dict would be.
Sad - ly and slow, But said He un - heed-ing - ly, Head bend-ing low.
"Let the first stone Come from the sin - less hands, Hence and a - lone."
Head bending low, He Who the world des-pised Bade her sin no more.
Soul, sick and sore; Go forth, I par - don thee; Go and sin no more.

CHORUS

"Nei-ther do I condemn, thee," Precious words di - vine; From the lips of

mer - cy Like the sweet-est chimes. Wonder - ful words of Je - sus,

Sing them o'er and o'er; "Neither do I con-demn thee, Go and sin no more.

Work for the Night Is Coming 224

Annie L. Walker

Lowell Mason

1. Work, for the night is com-ing, Work thru the morn-ing hours; Work while the
2. Work, for the night is com-ing, Work thru the sun - ny noon; Fill bright-est
3. Work, for the night is com-ing, Un - der the sun - set skies; While their bright

dew is sparkling, Work, 'mid springing flow'rs. Work when the day grows bright-er,
hours with la - bor, Rest comes sure and soon. Give ev - 'ry fly - ing min - ute,
tints are glowing, Work for day-light flies. Work till the last beam fad - eth,

Work in the glow-ing sun; Work, for the night is coming, When man's work is done.
Something to keep in store; Work, for the night is coming, When man works no more.
Fadeth to shine no more; Work, while the night is dark'ning; When man's work is o'er.

225 Life's Railway to Heaven

M. E. Abbey

Charlie D. Tillman
Arranged by John T. Benson, Jr.

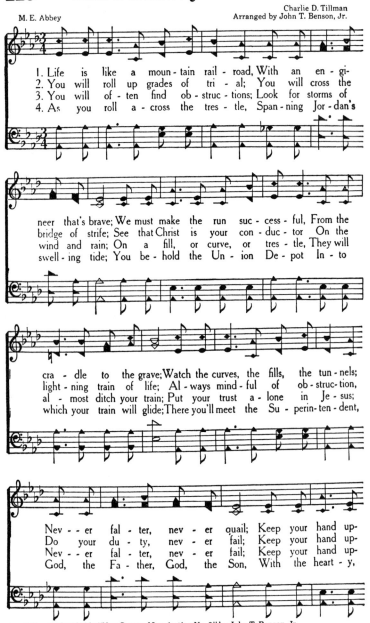

1. Life is like a moun-tain rail-road, With an en-gi-
2. You will roll up grades of tri - al; You will cross the
3. You will of - ten find ob - struc - tions; Look for storms of
4. As you roll a - cross the tres - tle, Span-ning Jor - dan's

neer that's brave; We must make the run suc-cess-ful, From the
bridge of strife; See that Christ is your con - duc - tor On the
wind and rain; On a fill, or curve, or tres - tle, They will
swell - ing tide; You be - hold the Un - ion De - pot In - to

cra - dle to the grave; Watch the curves, the fills, the tun - nels;
light - ning train of life; Al - ways mind - ful of ob - struc - tion,
al - most ditch your train; Put your trust a - lone in Je - sus;
which your train will glide; There you'll meet the Su - perin - ten - dent,

Nev - - er fal - ter, nev - er quail; Keep your hand up-
Do your du - ty, nev - er fail; Keep your hand up-
Nev - - er fal - ter, nev - er fail; Keep your hand up-
God, the Fa - ther, God, the Son, With the heart - y,

on the throt-tle, And your eye up-on the rail.
on the throt-tle, And your eye up-on the rail. Bless-ed Sav-ior,
on the throt-tle, And your eye up-on the rail.
joy - ous plaud-it, "Wea - ry pil - grim, wel-come home.

Thou wilt guide us Till we reach that bliss - ful shore, Where the

an - gels wait to join us In Thy praise for - ev - er - more.

Jesus, Lover of My Soul 226

Charles Wesley

S. B. Marsh

1 Je - sus, lov - er of my soul, Let me to Thy bos-om fly, Hide me, O my
   While the near-er wa-ters roll, While the tempest still is high; Till the storm of
2 Oth - er ref - uge have I none, Hangs my helpless soul on Thee; All my trust on,
   Leave, O leave me not a - lone, Still support and comfort me. All my help from
3 Plenteous grace with Thee is found, Grace to cover all my sin. Thou of life the
   Let the healing streams abound, Make and keep me pure within. Free - ly let me

Sav - ior hide,
life is past;   Safe in - to the ha-ven guide, O re-ceive my soul at last.
Thee is stayed,
Thee I bring,   Cov - er my defenceless head With the shadow of Thy wing,
Foun-tain art,
take of Thee,   Spring Thou up within my heart, Rise to all e - ter - ni - ty.

227   I've Never Loved Him Better

H. S.

Henry Slaughter

1. Since Je - sus came and found me and put His arms a - round me, And
2. Oh, bless - ed Friend Su - per - nal, my hope and joy e - ter - nal, Keep

all my bind-ing fet - ters took a - way. Al - though I've loved Him
Thou my soul 'til shad-ows flee a- way. For night-ly I would

dear - ly and trust - ed Him sin-cere - ly, I've nev-er loved Him
pray, Lord, 'Til end this pil-grim way, Lord,

CHORUS

bet - ter than to - day. I've nev-er loved Him bet-ter than to - day, I've

nev-er felt Him clos-er on the way: And oh! how sweet the feeling when

in His presence kneeling, I've never loved Him bet-ter than today.

What a Precious Friend   228

H. S.

Henry Slaughter

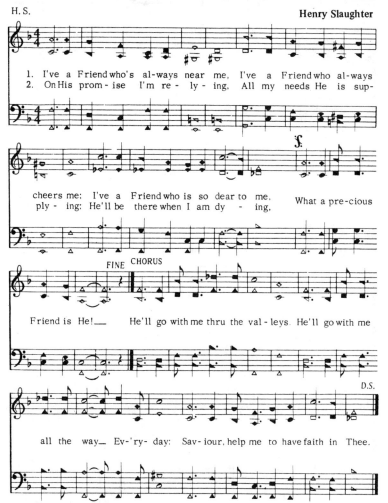

1. I've a Friend who's al-ways near me, I've a Friend who al-ways
2. On His prom-ise I'm re-ly-ing, All my needs He is sup-

cheers me; I've a Friend who is so dear to me,   What a pre-cious
ply-ing; He'll be there when I am dy - ing,

FINE   CHORUS

Friend is He!__   He'll go with me thru the val-leys. He'll go with me

D.S.

all the way__ Ev-'ry-day: Sav-iour, help me to have faith in Thee.

229 The Time Is Now

W. E. M.

W. Elmo Mercer

ad lib

1. Pa - tient - ly Je - sus is call - ing you, Let noth - ing stand in
2. Life ev - er - last - ing is of - fered you, God will for - give ev-

your way ___ Think of the cost: e - ter - nal - ly lost! But you can be
'ry sin ___ Trust and be - lieve, sal - va - tion re - ceive The mo-ment you

CHORUS a tempo

saved to - day. The time is now, the Lord is here, Won't you
let Him in.

o - pen your heart while He is near; His will o - bey, oh don't

1—D.C.— 2—FINE

de - lay! For sure - ly the time is now. ... now.

The Savior Is Waiting

230

R. C.

Ralph Carmichael

1. The Sav-ior is wait-ing to en-ter your heart— Why don't you
2. If you'll take one step toward the Sav-ior, my friend, You'll find His

let Him come in? There's nothing in this world to keep you a-
arms o - pen wide; Re-ceive Him and all of your darkness will

CHORUS

part— What is your an-swer to Him? Time af-ter time He has
end, With-in your heart He'll a - bide.

wait-ed be-fore, And now He is wait-ing a - gain To see if you're

will-ing to o- pen the door— O how He wants to come in!

231 Jesus Is Calling

Fanny J. Crosby

George C. Stebbins

1. Je - sus is ten - der - ly call - ing thee home— Call - ing to - day,
2. Je - sus is call - ing the wea - ry to rest— Call - ing to - day,
3. Je - sus is wait - ing, O come to Him now— Wait - ing to - day,
4. Je - sus is plead - ing, O list to His voice— Hear Him to - day,

call - ing to - day; Why from the sun-shine of love wilt thou roam
call - ing to - day; Bring Him thy bur - den and thou shalt be blest;
wait - ing to - day; Come with thy sins, at His feet low - ly bow;
hear Him to - day; They who be - lieve on His name shall re - joice;

CHORUS

Far - ther and far - ther a - way? Call - ing to - day!
He will not turn you a - way.
Come, and no long - er de - lay.
Quick - ly a - rise and a - way. Call - ing, call - ing to - day, to - day!

Call - ing to - day! Je - sus is
Call - ing, call - ing to - day, to - day! Je - sus is ten - der - ly

call - ing, Is ten - der - ly call - ing to - day.
call - ing to - day,

Softly and Tenderly

232

W. L. T.

Will L. Thompson

1. Soft - ly and ten - der - ly Je - sus is call - ing, Call - ing for
2. Why should we tar - ry when Je - sus is plead - ing, Plead - ing for
3. Time now is fleet - ing, the mo - ments are pass - ing, Pass - ing from
4. O for the won - der - ful love He has prom - ised, Prom - ised for

you and for me; See on the por - tals He's wait - ing and watch - ing,
you and for me? Why should we lin - ger and heed not His mer - cies,
you and from me; Shad - ows are gath - er - ing, death beds are com - ing,
you and for me; Tho we have sinned He has mer - cy and par - don,

CHORUS

Watch - ing for you and for me. Come home, come
Mer - cies for you and for me?
Com - ing for you and for me.
Par - don for you and for me. Come home,

home, Ye who are wea - ry, come home, Ear - nest - ly
come home,

ten - der - ly, Je - sus is call - ing, Call - ing, O sin - ner, come home.

233   Lord, I'm Coming Home

W. J. K.

Wm. J. Kirkpatrick

1. I've wan-dered far a-way from God, Now I'm com-ing home;
2. I've wast-ed man-y pre-cious years, Now I'm com-ing home;
3. I'm tired of sin and stray-ing, Lord, Now I'm com-ing home;
4. My soul is sick, my heart is sore, Now I'm com-ing home;
5. My on-ly hope, my on-ly plea, Now I'm com-ing home;
6. I need His cleans-ing blood, I know, Now I'm com-ing home;

The paths of sin too long I've trod, Lord, I'm com-ing home.
I now re-pent with bit-ter tears, Lord, I'm com-ing home.
I'll trust Thy love, be-lieve Thy word, Lord, I'm com-ing home.
My strength re-new, my hope re-store, Lord, I'm com-ing home.
That Je-sus died, and died for me, Lord, I'm com-ing home.
O wash me whi-ter than the snow, Lord, I'm com-ing home.

CHORUS

Com-ing home, com-ing home, Nev-er-more to roam;

O-pen wide Thine arms of love, Lord, I'm com-ing home.

There's a Great Day Coming   234

W. L. T.   W. L. Thompson

1. There's a great day com-ing, a great day com-ing, There's a great day
2. There's a bright day com-ing, a bright day com-ing, There's a bright day
3. There's a sad day com-ing, a sad day com-ing, There's a sad day

com-ing by and by, When the saints and the sin-ners shall be
com-ing by and by, But its bright-ness shall on - ly come to
com-ing by and by, When the sin - ner shall hear his doom, "De-

part - ed, right and left,
them that love the Lord, Are you read - y for that day to come?
part, I know ye not,"

Chorus

Are you read - y, are you read - y? Are you read - y for the

judgment day? Are you ready, are you ready For the judgment day?

235 I Gave My Life for Thee

Frances R. Havergal

P. P. Bliss

1. I gave My life for thee, My pre-cious blood I shed,
2. My Fa-ther's house of light, My glo-ry-cir-cled throne,
3. I suf-fered much for thee, More than thy tongue can tell,
4. And I have bro't to thee, Down from My home a-bove,

That thou might'st ran-somed be, And quick-ened from the dead;
I left for earth-ly night, For wan-d'rings sad and lone;
Of bit-t'rest ag-o-ny, To res-cue thee from hell;
Sal-va-tion full and free, My par-don and My love;

I gave, I gave My life for thee, What hast thou giv'n for Me?
I left, I left it all for thee, Hast thou left aught for Me?
I've borne, I've borne it all for thee, What hast thou borne for Me?
I bring, I bring rich gifts to thee, What hast thou bro't for Me?

236 Pass Me Not

Fanny J. Crosby

W. H. Doane

1. Pass me not, O gen-tle Sav-ior, Hear my hum-ble cry; While on oth-ers
2. Let me at a throne of mer-cy Find a sweet re-lief; Kneel-ing there in
3. Trust-ing on-ly in Thy mer-it, Would I seek Thy face; Heal my wounded,
4. Thou the Spring of all my com-fort, More than life to me, Whom have I on

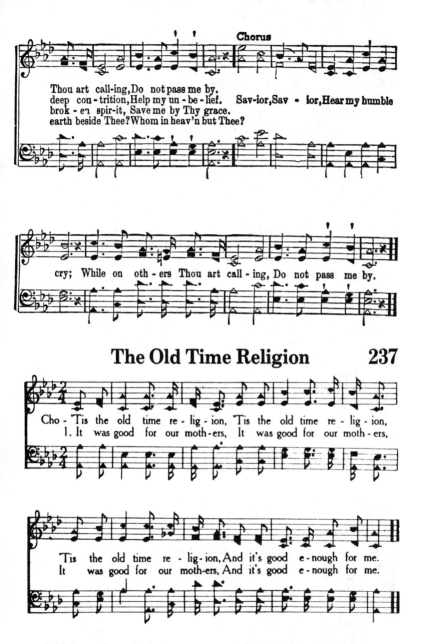

Chorus

Thou art call-ing, Do not pass me by.

deep con-trition, Help my un-be-lief. Sav-ior, Sav-ior, Hear my humble

brok-en spir-it, Save me by Thy grace.

earth beside Thee? Whom in heav'n but Thee?

cry; While on oth-ers Thou art call-ing, Do not pass me by.

The Old Time Religion   237

Cho-'Tis the old time re-lig-ion, 'Tis the old time re-lig-ion,

1. It was good for our moth-ers, It was good for our moth-ers,

'Tis the old time re-lig-ion, And it's good e-nough for me.

It was good for our moth-ers, And it's good e-nough for me.

2. Makes me love ev'ry-body.
3. It has saved our fathers.
4. It was good for the Prophet Daniel.
5. It was good for the Hebrew children.

6. It was tried in the fiery furnace.
7. It was good for Paul and Silas.
8. It will do when I am dying.
9. It will take us all to heaven.

238 Glory to His Name

Rev. E. A. Hoffman
Rev. J. H. Stockton

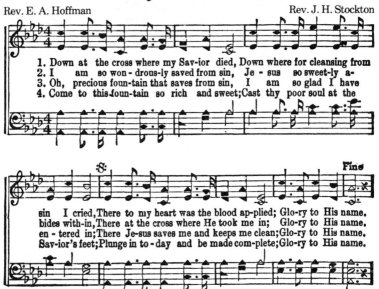

1. Down at the cross where my Sav-ior died, Down where for cleansing from
2. I am so won-drous-ly saved from sin, Je-sus so sweet-ly a-
3. Oh, precious foun-tain that saves from sin, I am so glad I have
4. Come to this foun-tain so rich and sweet; Cast thy poor soul at the

sin I cried, There to my heart was the blood ap-plied; Glo-ry to His name.
bides with-in, There at the cross where He took me in; Glo-ry to His name.
en-tered in; There Je-sus saves me and keeps me clean; Glo-ry to His name.
Sav-ior's feet; Plunge in to-day and be made com-plete; Glo-ry to His name.

D. S. There to my heart was the blood ap-plied; Glo-ry to His name.

Chorus

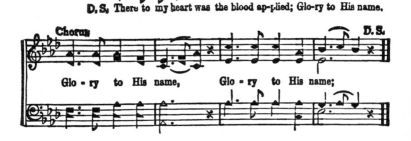

Glo-ry to His name, Glo-ry to His name;

239 I Am Coming to the Cross

W. H. McDonald
Wm. G. Fischer

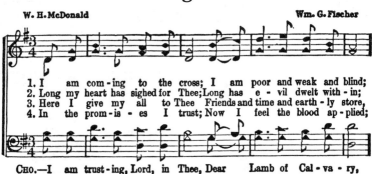

1. I am com-ing to the cross; I am poor and weak and blind;
2. Long my heart has sighed for Thee; Long has e-vil dwelt with-in;
3. Here I give my all to Thee Friends and time and earth-ly store,
4. In the prom-is-es I trust; Now I feel the blood ap-plied;

Cho.—I am trust-ing, Lord, in Thee, Dear Lamb of Cal-va-ry,

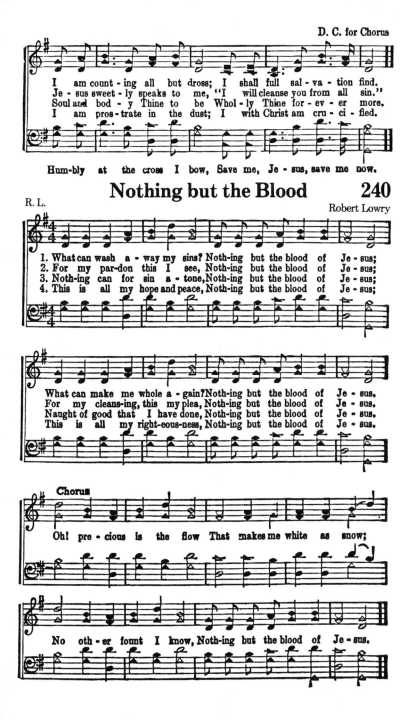

I am count-ing all but dross; I shall full sal-va-tion find,
Je-sus sweet-ly speaks to me, "I will cleanse you from all sin."
Soul and bod-y Thine to be Whol-ly Thine for-ev-er more.
I am pros-trate in the dust; I with Christ am cru-ci-fied.

Hum-bly at the cross I bow, Save me, Je-sus, save me now.

Nothing but the Blood   240

R. L.

Robert Lowry

1. What can wash a-way my sins? Noth-ing but the blood of Je-sus;
2. For my par-don this I see, Noth-ing but the blood of Je-sus;
3. Noth-ing can for sin a-tone, Noth-ing but the blood of Je-sus;
4. This is all my hope and peace, Noth-ing but the blood of Je-sus;

What can make me whole a-gain? Noth-ing but the blood of Je-sus.
For my cleans-ing, this my plea, Noth-ing but the blood of Je-sus.
Naught of good that I have done, Noth-ing but the blood of Je-sus.
This is all my right-eous-ness, Noth-ing but the blood of Je-sus.

Chorus

Oh! pre-cious is the flow That makes me white as snow;

No oth-er fount I know, Noth-ing but the blood of Je-sus.

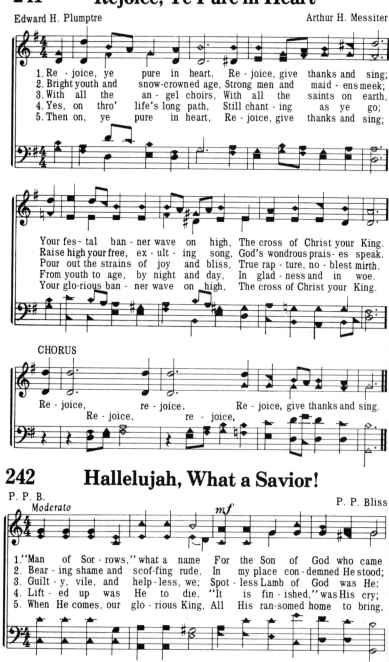

241 Rejoice, Ye Pure in Heart

Edward H. Plumptre

Arthur H. Messiter

1. Re - joice, ye pure in heart, Re - joice, give thanks and sing;
2. Bright youth and snow-crowned age, Strong men and maid - ens meek;
3. With all the an - gel choirs, With all the saints on earth,
4. Yes, on thro' life's long path, Still chant - ing as ye go;
5. Then on, ye pure in heart, Re - joice, give thanks and sing;

Your fes - tal ban - ner wave on high, The cross of Christ your King.
Raise high your free, ex - ult - ing song, God's wondrous prais- es speak.
Pour out the strains of joy and bliss, True rap - ture, no - blest mirth.
From youth to age, by night and day, In glad - ness and in woe.
Your glo-rious ban - ner wave on high, The cross of Christ your King.

CHORUS

Re - joice, re - joice, Re - joice, give thanks and sing.
Re - joice, re - joice,

242 Hallelujah, What a Savior!

P. P. B.

P. P. Bliss

Moderato
mf

1. "Man of Sor - rows," what a name For the Son of God who came
2. Bear - ing shame and scof - fing rude, In my place con - demned He stood;
3. Guilt - y, vile, and help - less, we: Spot - less Lamb of God was He:
4. Lift - ed up was He to die, "It is fin - ished," was His cry;
5. When He comes, our glo - rious King, All His ran - somed home to bring,

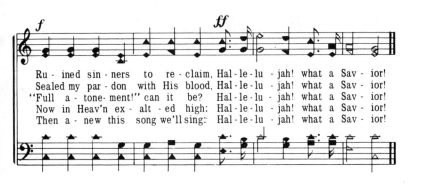

Ru - ined sin - ners to re - claim, Hal - le - lu - jah! what a Sav - ior!
Sealed my par - don with His blood, Hal - le - lu - jah! what a Sav - ior!
"Full a - tone - ment!" can it be? Hal - le - lu - jah! what a Sav - ior!
Now in Heav'n ex - alt - ed high: Hal - le - lu - jah! what a Sav - ior!
Then a - new this song we'll sing: Hal - le - lu - jah! what a Sav - ior!

What Did He Do? 243

Anon. Alt.   W. Owen

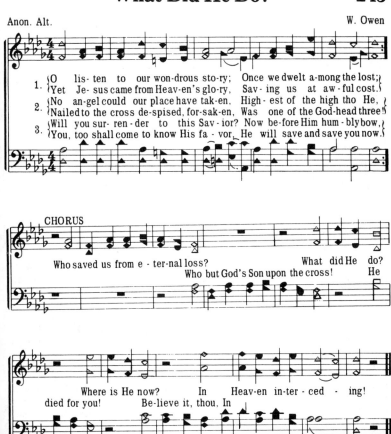

1. {O lis- ten to our won-drous sto-ry; Once we dwelt a-mong the lost;}
   {Yet Je- sus came from Heav-en's glo-ry, Sav- ing us at aw - ful cost.}
2. {No an-gel could our place have tak-en, High- est of the high tho He,}
   {Nailed to the cross de-spised, for-sak-en, Was one of the God-head three!}
3. {Will you sur - ren - der to this Sav-ior? Now be-fore Him hum - bly bow,}
   {You, too shall come to know His fa - vor, He will save and save you now.}

CHORUS

Who saved us from e - ter-nal loss?   What did He do?
Who but God's Son upon the cross!   He

Where is He now?   In   Heav-en in-ter- ced - ing!
died for you!   Be-lieve it, thou, In

244 Hallelujah for the Cross

Horatius Bonar

James McGranahan

1. The Cross, it stand - eth fast, Hal - le - lu - jah! Hal - le - lu - jah!
2. It is the old Cross still, Hal - le - lu - jah! Hal - le - lu - jah!
3. 'Twas here the debt was paid, Hal - le - lu - jah! Hal - le - lu - jah!

De - fy - ing ev - 'ry blast, Hal - le - lu - jah! Hal - le - lu - jah!
Its tri - umph let us tell, Hal - le - lu - jah! Hal - le - lu - jah!
Our sins on Je - sus laid, Hal - le - lu - jah! Hal - le - lu - jah!

The winds of hell have blown, The world its hate hath shown,
The grace of God here shown Through Christ, the bless - ed Son,
So round the Cross we sing Of Christ, our Of - fer - ing;

Yet it is not o - ver-thrown. Hal - le - lu - jah for the Cross!
Who did for sin a - tone! Hal - le - lu - jah for the Cross!
Of Christ, our liv - ing King. Hal - le - lu - jah for the Cross!

CHORUS

Hal - le - lu - jah, hal - le - lu - jah, hal - le - lu - jah for the Cross!

Hal - le - lu - jah, hal - le - lu - jah! It shall nev - er suf - fer loss!

Christ Arose

245

R. L.

Robert Lowry

1. Low in the grave He lay– Je - sus, my Sav-ior! Wait-ing the com-ing day–
2. Vain - ly they watch His bed– Je - sus, my Sav-ior! Vain - ly they seal the dead–
3. Death can-not keep His prey– Je - sus, my Sav-ior! He tore the bars a - way–

CHORUS

Je - sus, my Lord! Up from the grave He a-rose, With a might - y triumph o'er His
He a-rose,

foes; He arose a vic-tor from the dark domain, And He lives for-ev - er with His
He arose

saints to reign; He a-rose! He a-rose! Hal-le - lu - jah! Christ a-rose!
He a-rose! He arose!

246 One Day

J. Wilbur Chapman

Charles H. Marsh

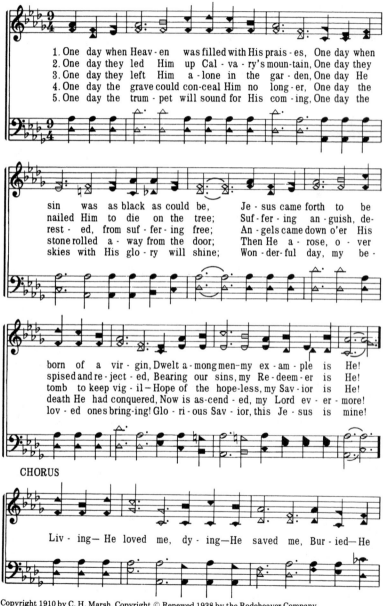

1. One day when Heav-en was filled with His prais-es, One day when sin was as black as could be, Je-sus came forth to be born of a vir-gin, Dwelt a-mong men—my ex-am-ple is He!

2. One day they led Him up Cal-va-ry's moun-tain, One day they nailed Him to die on the tree; Suf-fer-ing an-guish, de-spised and re-ject-ed, Bearing our sins, my Re-deem-er is He!

3. One day they left Him a-lone in the gar-den, One day He rest-ed, from suf-fer-ing free; An-gels came down o'er His tomb to keep vig-il—Hope of the hope-less, my Sav-ior is He!

4. One day the grave could con-ceal Him no long-er, One day the stone rolled a-way from the door; Then He a-rose, o-ver death He had conquered, Now is as-cend-ed, my Lord ev-er-more!

5. One day the trum-pet will sound for His com-ing, One day the skies with His glo-ry will shine; Won-der-ful day, my be-lov-ed ones bring-ing! Glo-ri-ous Sav-ior, this Je-sus is mine!

CHORUS

Liv-ing—He loved me, dy-ing—He saved me, Bur-ied—He

car - ried my sins far a - way; Ris - ing—He jus - ti - fied

free - ly, for - ev - er: One day He's com - ing— O glo - ri - ous day!

Where He Leads Me 247

E. W. Blandly

J. S. Norris

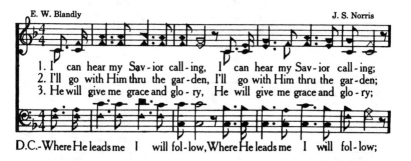

1. I can hear my Sav - ior call - ing, I can hear my Sav - ior call - ing;
2. I'll go with Him thru the gar - den, I'll go with Him thru the gar - den;
3. He will give me grace and glo - ry, He will give me grace and glo - ry;

D.C.-Where He leads me I will fol - low, Where He leads me I will fol - low;

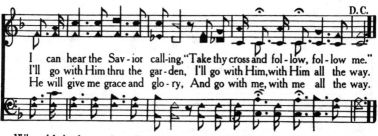

I can hear the Sav - ior call - ing, "Take thy cross and fol - low, fol - low me."
I'll go with Him thru the gar - den, I'll go with Him, with Him all the way.
He will give me grace and glo - ry, And go with me, with me all the way.

Where He leads me I will fol - low, I'll go with Him, with Him all the way

248 Greater Is He that Is in Me

L.W.

Lanny Wolfe

REFRAIN:

D. C. Great-er is He ___ that is in me, Greater is He ___ that is

in me, Greater is He ___ that is in me than he that is in ___

FINE   **VERSE:** (Cue notes for 2nd verse)

the world. 1. Sa - tan's like ___ a roar-ing lion ___
2. On the ___ day of ___ Pen - te - cost ___ a

roam - ing to ___ and ___ fro, Seek-ing whom he may
rush - ing ___ might - y wind ___ Blew in - to the up-

de - vour, ___ the Bi - ble tells me so; ___ Man - y souls have
per room ___ and bap-tized all of them; ___ With a pow - er

been his prey — to fall in some weak hour, — But God has
great-er than — — an-y earth-ly foe, — And I'm so

D. C.

promised us to - day — — — His o-ver-com-ing pow'r. —
glad I've got it, too, — — I'm gon-na let the whole world know. —

I Need Thee Every Hour 249

Mrs. Annie S. Hawks   Rev. Robert Lowry

1. I need Thee ev - 'ry hour, Most gra - cious Lord; No ten - der voice like
2. I need Thee ev - 'ry hour, Stay Thou near by; Temp-ta-tions lose their
3. I need Thee ev - 'ry hour, In joy or pain; Come quick-ly and a-
4. I need Thee ev - 'ry hour, Most Ho - ly One; O make me Thine in-

Chorus

Thine Can peace af - ford.
pow'r When Thou art nigh. I need Thee, O I need Thee; Ev-'ry hour I
bide, Or life is vain.
deed, Thou bless - ed Son.

need Thee! O bless me now, my Sav - ior, I come to Thee!

250 The Way of the Cross Leads Home

Jessie Brown Pounds

Chas. H. Gabriel

1. I must needs go home by the way of the cross, There's no oth-er
2. I must needs go on in the blood-sprinkled way, The path that the
3. Then I bid fare-well to the way of the world, To walk in it

way but this; I shall ne'er get sight of the Gates of Light
Sav-ior trod, If I ev-er climb to the heights sublime,
nev-er-more; For my Lord says "Come," and I seek my home,

If the way of the cross I miss.
Where the soul is at home with God.
Where He waits at the o-pen door.

CHORUS

The way of the cross leads
home, The way of the cross leads home; It is
leads home, leads home;

sweet to know, as I on-ward go, The way of the cross leads home.

No Tears in Heaven

251

R. S. A.

Robert S. Arnold

1. No tears in Heav-en, no sor-rows giv-en, All will be glo-ry in that land;....There'll be no sad-ness, all will be glad-ness, When we shall join that hap-py band.......

2. Glo-ry is wait-ing, wait-ing up yon-der, Where we shall spend an endless day;.....There with our Sav-ior, we'll be for-ev-er, Where no more sor-row can dis-may........

3. Some morn-ing yon-der, we'll cease to pon-der, O'er things this life has bro't to view;...All will be clear-er, loved ones be dear-er, In Heav'n where all will be made new.......

CHORUS

No tears.........................no tears, no tears up there, in Heav-en fair,

Sor-row and pain will all have flown;........... No tears,........................ in Heav-en fair,

no tears, no tears up there, No tears in Heav-en will be known.

252 The Healer

L. I.

Lois Irwin

1. On the Cross cru-ci-fied, In great sor-row He died; The
2. Price for heal-ing was paid, As those cruel stripes were made, With-
3. Came the lep-er to Christ, Say-ing "Sure-ly I know, That
4. He has healed my sick soul, Made me ev-'ry whit whole, And

Giv-er of life was He— Yet my Lord was de-spised and re-
in Pi-late's judg-ment hall.— Now His suf-f'ring af-ford per-fect
Thou, Lord, canst make me whole."— When His great faith was seen Je-sus
He'll do the same to you.— He's the same yes-ter-day and to-

Chorus

ject-ed of men, This Je-sus of Cal-va-ry.
heal-ing for all. This won-der-ful Heal-er's mine. He was wound-ed for
said, "Yes, I will." And touched him and made him clean.
day and for aye, This Heal-er of men to-day.

our trans-gres-sions, He was bruised for our in-iq-ui-ties;

Sure-ly He bore our sor-rows, And by His stripes we are healed.

There Shall Be Showers of Blessing 253

Daniel W. Whittle

James McGranahan

1. "There shall be show-ers of bless-ing" This is the prom-ise of love;
2. "There shall be show-ers of bless-ing" Pre - cious, re - viv-ing a - gain,
3. "There shall be show-ers of bless-ing" Send them up - on us, O Lord!
4. "There shall be show-ers of bless-ing" O that to - day they might fall,

There shall be sea-sons re-fresh - ing, Sent from the Sav - ior a - bove.
O - ver the hills and the val - leys Sound of a - bun-dance of rain.
Grant to us now a re - fresh - ing, Come and now hon - or Thy Word!
Now as to God we're con-fess - ing, Now as on Je - sus we call!

CHORUS

Show   ers of bless-ing, Show -ers of bless-ing we need;
Show - ers, show-ers

Mer - cy-drops round us are fall - ing, But for the show-ers we plead.

254 Onward, Christian Soldiers

Sabine Gould

A. S. Sullivan

1. On - ward, Christian sol - diers, Marching as to war, With the cross of
2. At the sign of tri - umph, Sa - tan's host doth flee; On, then, Christian
3. Like a might - y ar - my, Moves the Church of God; Broth-ers, we are
4. On - ward, then, ye peo - ple, Join our hap - py throng; Blend with ours your

Je - sus, Go - ing on be - fore; Christ, the roy - al Mas - ter,
sol - diers, On to vic - to - ry! Hell's foun - da - tions quiv - er
tread - ing Where the saints have trod; We are not di - vid - ed,
voic - es In the tri - umph song; Glo - ry, laud, and hon - or,

Leads a - gainst the foe; For - ward in - to bat - tle See His ban - ner go.
At the shout of praise; Brothers, lift your voic - es, Loud your anthems raise!
All one bod - y we, One in hope and doc - trine, One in char - i - ty.
Un - to Christ, the King; This thru countless a - ges, Men and an - gels sing.

CHORUS

On - ward, Chris - tian sol - diers, March - ing as to

war, With the cross of Je - sus Go - ing on be - fore.

I Will Sing the Wondrous Story   255

Francis H. Rowley

Peter Bilhorn

1. I will sing the won-drous sto-ry, Of the Christ who died for me,
2. I was lost, but Je-sus found me, Found the sheep that went a-stray,
3. I was bruised, but Je-sus healed me, Faint was I from many a fall,
4. Days of dark-ness still come o'er me, Sor-row's paths I oft-en tread.
5. He will keep me till the riv-er Rolls its wa-ters at my feet;

How He left His home in glo-ry, For the cross of Cal-va-ry.
Threw His lov-ing arms a-round me, Drew me back in-to His way.
Sight was gone, and fears possessed me, But He freed me from them all.
But the Sav-ior still is with me, By His hand I'm safe-ly led.
Then He'll bear me safe-ly o-ver, Where the loved ones I shall meet.

CHORUS

Yes, I'll sing.................the wondrous sto - ry Of the
Yes, I'll sing   the won-drous sto-ry,

Christ............who died for me,................Sing it with...........the saints in
Of the Christ   who died for me,   Sing it with

glo - ry Gathered by................the crystal sea.
the saints in glo-ry,   Gathered by   the crystal sea.

256 Heavenly Sunlight

H. J. Zelley

G. H. Cook

1. Walk-ing in sun-light, all of my jour-ney, O-ver the moun-tains,
2. Shad-ows a-round me, shad-ows a-bove me, Nev-er con-ceal my
3. In the bright sun-light, ev-er re-joic-ing, Press-ing my way to

thro' the deep vale; Je-sus has said, "I'll nev-er for-sake thee,"
Sav-ior and guide; He is the light, in Him is no dark-ness,
mansions a-bove; Sing-ing His prais-es, glad-ly I'm walk-ing,

CHORUS

Prom-ise di-vine that nev-er can fail.
Ev-er I'm walk-ing close to His side. Heav-en-ly sun-light,
Walk-ing in sun-light, sun-light of love.

Heav-en-ly sun-light, flood-ing my soul with glo-ry di-vine; Hal-le-

lu-jah, I am re-joic-ing, Sing-ing His prais-es, Je-sus is mine.

O That Will Be Glory

257

C. H. G.

Chas. H. Gabriel

1. When all my la - bors and tri - als are o'er, And I am safe on that beau - ti - ful shore, Just to be near the dear Lord I a - dore,
2. When, by the gift of His in - fi - nite grace, I am ac - cord - ed in heav - en a place, Just to be there and to look on His face,
3. Friends will be there I have loved long a - go, Joy like a riv - er a - round me will flow; Yet, just a smile from my Sav - ior, I know,

rit.

Will thru the a - ges be glo - ry for me..........

CHORUS

O that will be glo - ry for me, Glo - ry for me, glo - ry for me; When by His grace

O............... that will be glory for me, glo - ry for me, glo - ry for me;...................

rit

I shall look on His face, That will be glo - ry, be glo - ry for me!

258   Safe in the Arms of Jesus

Fanny J. Crosby

W. H. Doane

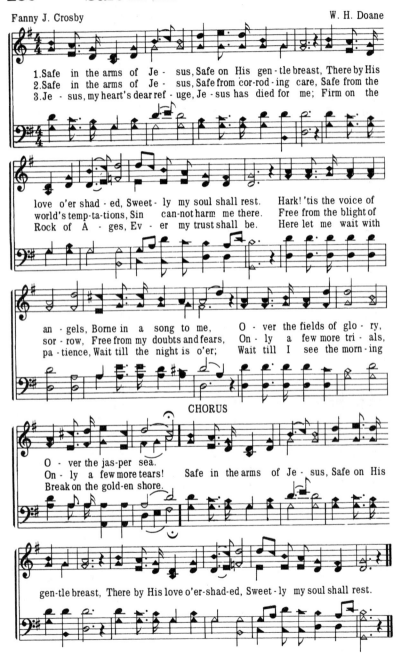

1. Safe in the arms of Je - sus, Safe on His gen - tle breast, There by His
2. Safe in the arms of Je - sus, Safe from cor-rod - ing care, Safe from the
3. Je - sus, my heart's dear ref - uge, Je - sus has died for me; Firm on the

love o'er shad - ed, Sweet - ly my soul shall rest.   Hark! 'tis the voice of
world's temp-ta-tions, Sin can-not harm me there.   Free from the blight of
Rock of A - ges, Ev - er my trust shall be.   Here let me wait with

an - gels, Borne in a song to me,   O - ver the fields of glo - ry,
sor - row, Free from my doubts and fears,   On - ly a few more tri - als,
pa - tience, Wait till the night is o'er;   Wait till I see the morn - ing

CHORUS

O - ver the jas-per sea.
On - ly a few more tears!   Safe in the arms of Je - sus, Safe on His
Break on the gold-en shore.

gen-tle breast, There by His love o'er-shad-ed, Sweet - ly my soul shall rest.

He Hideth My Soul

259

Fanny J. Crosby

William J. Kirkpatrick

1. A won-der-ful Sav-ior is Je-sus, my Lord, A won-der-ful
2. A won-der-ful Sav-ior is Je-sus, my Lord, He tak-eth my
3. With num-ber-less blessings each mo-ment He crowns, And, filled with His
4. When clothed in His brightness, trans-port-ed I rise To meet Him in

Sav-ior to me; He hid-eth my soul in the cleft of the rock, Where
bur-den a-way; He hold-eth me up, and I shall not be moved, He
full-ness di-vine, I sing in my rap-ture, oh, glo-ry to God For
clouds of the sky, His per-fect sal-va-tion, His won-der-ful love, I'll

CHORUS

riv-ers of pleas-ure I see.
giv-eth me strength as my day. He hid-eth my soul in the cleft of the rock
such a Re-deem-er as mine!
shout with the mil-lions on high.

That shadows a dry, thirst-y land; He hid-eth my life in the depths of His love,

And cov-ers me there with His hand, And cov-ers me there with His hand.

260 Jesus, I Come

William T. Sleeper

George C. Stebbins

1. Out of my bond-age, sor-row and night, Je-sus, I come, Je-sus, I come;
2. Out of my shame-ful fail-ure and loss, Je-sus, I come, Je-sus, I come;
3. Out of un-rest and ar-ro-gant pride, Je-sus, I come, Je-sus, I come;
4. Out of the fear and dread of the tomb, Je-sus, I come, Je-sus, I come;

In - to Thy free-dom, glad-ness and light, Je-sus, I come to Thee.
In - to the glo-rious gain of Thy cross, Je-sus, I come to Thee.
In - to Thy bless-ed will to a - bide, Je-sus, I come to Thee.
In - to the joy and light of Thy home, Je-sus, I come to Thee.

Out of my sick-ness, in-to Thy health, Out of my want and in - to Thy wealth,
Out of earth's sorrows, in-to Thy balm, Out of life's storms and in - to Thy calm,
Out of my-self to dwell in Thy love, Out of de-spair in-to rap-tures a-bove,
Out of the depths of ru-in un-told, In-to the peace of Thy shel-ter-ing fold,

Out of my sin and in-to Thy-self, Je-sus, I come to Thee.
Out of dis-tress to ju-bi-lant psalm, Je-sus, I come to Thee.
Up-ward for aye on wings like a dove, Je-sus, I come to Thee.
Ev-er Thy glo-rious face to be-hold, Je-sus, I come to Thee.

Rescue the Perishing

Fannie J. Crosby

William H. Doane

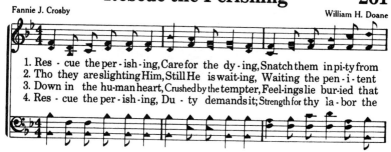

1. Res - cue the per - ish - ing, Care for the dy - ing, Snatch them in pi - ty from
2. Tho they are slighting Him, Still He is wait - ing, Waiting the pen - i - tent
3. Down in the hu - man heart, Crushed by the tempter, Feel-ings lie bur - ied that
4. Res - cue the per - ish - ing, Du - ty demands it; Strength for thy la - bor the

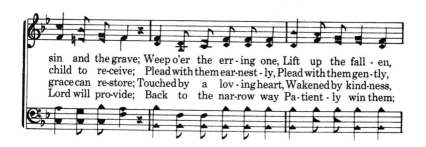

sin and the grave; Weep o'er the err - ing one, Lift up the fall - en,
child to re - ceive; Plead with them earn-est - ly, Plead with them gen - tly,
grace can re - store; Touched by a lov - ing heart, Wakened by kind-ness,
Lord will pro-vide; Back to the nar-row way Pa - tient - ly win them;

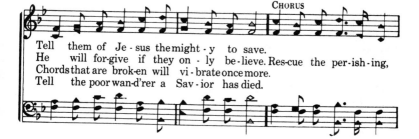

CHORUS

Tell them of Je - sus the might - y to save.
He will for-give if they on - ly be - lieve. Res-cue the per - ish - ing,
Chords that are brok-en will vi - brate once more.
Tell the poor wan-d'rer a Sav - ior has died.

Care for the dy - ing; Je - sus is mer - ci - ful, Je - sus will save.

262 Throw Out the Lifeline

Rev. Edward S. Ufford

E. S. U. Arr. by Geo. C. Stebbins

1. Throw out the Life-line a-cross the dark wave, There is a broth-er whom some one should save; Some-bod-y's broth-er! O who then will dare To throw out the Life-line, His per-il to share?

2. Throw out the Life-line with hand quick and strong, Why do you tar-ry, why lin-ger so long? See! he is sink-ing; O has-ten to-day— And out with the Life-boat! a-way then a-way! Throw out the Life-line!

3. Throw out the Life-line to dan-ger-fraught men, Sinking in an-guish where you've nev-er been: Winds of temp-ta-tion and bil-lows of woe Will soon hurl them out where the dark wa-ters flow. throw out the Life-line and save them to-day.

4. Soon will the sea-son of res-cue be o'er, Soon will they drift to e-ter-ni-ty's shore, Haste then my broth-er, no time for de-lay, But

CHORUS

throw out the Life-line! Some one is drift-ing a-way; Throw out the Life-line! throw out the Life-line! Some one is sink-ing to-day.

Send the Light

C. H. G.

Chas. H. Gabriel

1. There's a call comes ring-ing o'er the rest-less wave, Send the light!
2. We have heard the Ma - ce - do - ian call to-day,
3. We will pray that grace may ev - 'ry-where a-bound,
4. We will not grow wea - ry in the work of love,

Send the light!

send the light!

There are souls to res - cue, there are
And a gold - en of - f'ring at the
And a Christ - like spir - it ev - 'ry-
send the light! Let us gath - er jew - els for a

souls to save, Send the light!
cross we lay,
where be found,
crown a - bove,

send the light!

Send the light!

send the light!

Chorus

Send the light! . . . . the bless - ed gos - pel light, Let it
Send the light! the bless - ed gos - pel light,

shine . . . . from shore to shore! . . . . for - ev - er-more.
Let it shine from shore to shore! for - ev - er-more.

264 Sweet By and By

S. Fillmore Bennett

Jos. P. Webster

1. There's a land that is fair-er than day, And by faith we can see it a-
2. We shall sing on that beau-ti-ful shore The mel-o-di-ous songs of the
3. To our boun-ti-ful Fa-ther a-bove, We will of-fer our trib-ute of

far; For the Fa-ther waits o-ver the way, To pre-pare us a
blest, And our spir-its shall sor-row no more, Not a sigh for the
praise, For the glo-ri-ous gift of His love And the bless-ings that

CHORUS

dwell-ing place there. In the sweet by and by, We shall
bless-ing of rest.
hal-low our days. In the sweet by and by,

meet on that beau-ti-ful shore; In the sweet by and
by and by; In the sweet

by, We shall meet on that beau-ti-ful shore.
by and by,

Will There Be Any Stars?

265

E. E. Hewitt

Jno. R. Sweney

1. I am think-ing to-day of that beau-ti-ful land I shall reach when the
2. In the strength of the Lord let me la-bor and pray, Let me watch as a
3. O what joy will it be when His face I be-hold, Liv-ing gems at His

sun go-eth down; When thro' won-der-ful grace by my Sav-ior I stand, Will there
win-ner of souls; That bright stars may be mine in the glo-ri-ous day, When His
feet to lay down; It would sweet-en my bliss in the cit-y of gold, Should there

Chorus

be an-y stars in my crown?
praise like the sea-bil-lows roll. Will there be an-y stars, an-y stars in my crown,
be an-y stars in my crown?

When at eve-ning the sun go-eth down? . . . . When I wake with the blest,
go-eth down?

In the man-sions of rest, Will there be an-y stars in my crown?
an-y stars in my crown?

266   It Took a Miracle

J. W. P.

John W. Peterson

1. My Fa - ther is om - ni - po - tent, And that you can't de - ny;
2. Tho here His glo - ry has been shown, We still can't ful - ly see
3. The Bi - ble tells us of His pow'r And wis - dom all way thru,

A God of might and mir - a - cles—'Tis writ - ten in the sky.
The won-ders of His might, His throne—'Twill take e - ter - ni - ty.
And ev - 'ry lit - tle bird and flow'r Are tes - ti - mon - ies too.

CHORUS

It took a mir - a - cle to put the stars in place, It took a

mir - a - cle to hang the world in space; But when He saved my soul,

Cleansed and made me whole, It took a mir - a - cle of love and grace.

Ring the Bells of Heaven! 267

William O. Cushing

George F. Root

1. Ring the bells of Heav - en! there is joy to - day For a soul re-
2. Ring the bells of Heav - en! there is joy to - day, For the wan-d'rer
3. Ring the bells of Heav - en! spread the feast to-day! An - gels, swell the

turn - ing from the wild! See! the Fa - ther meets him out up - on the way,
now is rec - on-ciled; Yes, a soul is res-cued from his sin - ful way,
glad tri - um-phant strain! Tell the joy - ful tid - ings, bear it far a - way!

CHORUS

Wel - com - ing His wea - ry, wan-d'ring child.
And is born a - new, a ran-somed child.   Glo - ry! glo - ry! how the
For a pre-cious soul is born a - gain.

an-gels sing; Glo-ry! glo - ry! how the loud harps ring! 'Tis the ran-somed

ar - my, like a might - y sea, Peal-ing forth the an - them of the free!

268   'Tis So Sweet to Trust in Jesus

Mrs. Louisa M. R. Stead

Wm. J. Kirkpatrick

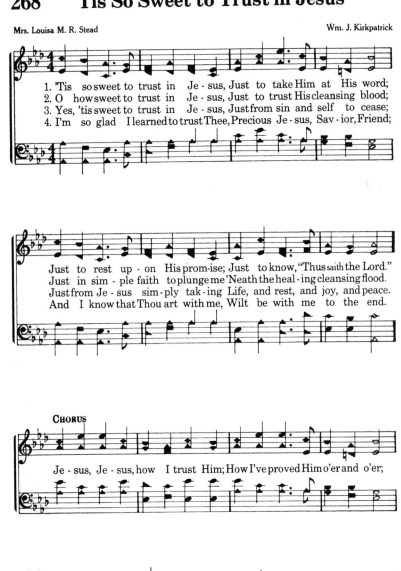

1. 'Tis so sweet to trust in Je-sus, Just to take Him at His word;
2. O how sweet to trust in Je-sus, Just to trust His cleansing blood;
3. Yes, 'tis sweet to trust in Je-sus, Just from sin and self to cease;
4. I'm so glad I learned to trust Thee, Precious Je-sus, Sav-ior, Friend;

Just to rest up-on His prom-ise; Just to know, "Thus saith the Lord."
Just in sim-ple faith to plunge me 'Neath the heal-ing cleansing flood.
Just from Je-sus sim-ply tak-ing Life, and rest, and joy, and peace.
And I know that Thou art with me, Wilt be with me to the end.

CHORUS

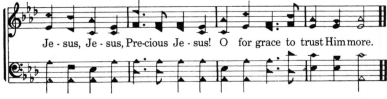

Je-sus, Je-sus, how I trust Him; How I've proved Him o'er and o'er;

Je-sus, Je-sus, Pre-cious Je-sus! O for grace to trust Him more.

Praise Him! Praise Him!

269

"I will Sing psalms unto my God." - Ps. 146:2

Fanny J. Crosby

Chester G. Allen

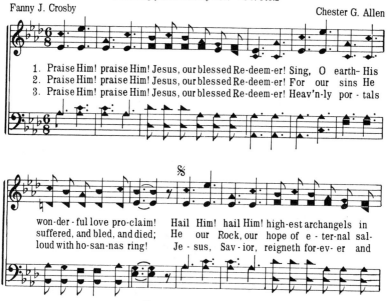

1. Praise Him! praise Him! Jesus, our blessed Re-deem-er! Sing, O earth- His
2. Praise Him! praise Him! Jesus, our blessed Re-deem-er! For our sins He
3. Praise Him! praise Him! Jesus, our blessed Re-deem-er! Heav'n-ly por-tals

won-der-ful love pro-claim! Hail Him! hail Him! high-est archangels in
suffered, and bled, and died; He our Rock, our hope of e-ter-nal sal-
loud with ho-san-nas ring! Je-sus, Sav-ior, reigneth for-ev-er and

D.S. - Praise Him! praise Him! tell of His ex-cel-lent

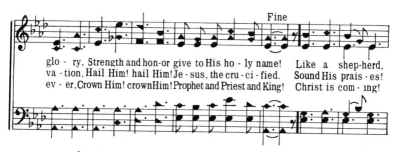

glo - ry, Strength and hon-or give to His ho - ly name! Like a shep-herd,
va - tion, Hail Him! hail Him! Je-sus, the cru-ci-fied. Sound His prais-es!
ev - er, Crown Him! crown Him! Prophet and Priest and King! Christ is com-ing!

Fine

greatness! Praise Him! praise Him! ev-er in joy-ful song!

D.S.

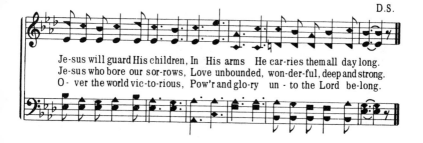

Je-sus will guard His children, In His arms He car-ries them all day long.
Je-sus who bore our sor-rows, Love unbounded, won-der-ful, deep and strong.
O - ver the world vic-to-rious, Pow'r and glo-ry un - to the Lord be-long.

270   Faith Is the Victory

John H. Yates

Ira D. Sankey

1. En-camped a - long the hills of light, Ye Chris-tian sol - diers, rise,
2. His ban - ner o - ver us is love, Our sword the Word of God;
3. On ev - 'ry hand the foe we find Drawn up in dread ar - ray;

And press the bat - tle ere the night Shall veil the glow - ing skies;
We tread the road the saints a - bove With shouts of tri - umph trod;
Let tents of ease be left be - hind, And on - ward to the fray;

A - gainst the foe in vales be - low, Let all our strength be hurled;
By faith, they, like a whirl-wind's breath, Swept on o'er ev - 'ry field;
Sal - va - tion's hel-met on each head, With truth all girt a - bout,

Faith is the vic - to - ry, we know, That o - ver-comes the world.
The faith by which they conquer'd death Is still our shin - ing shield.
The earth shall trem-ble 'neath our tread, And ech-o with our shout.

CHORUS

Faith is the vic - to - ry! Faith is the vic - to - ry!

Oh, glo - ri - ous vic - to - ry That o - ver - comes the world.

More About Jesus

271

Eliza E. Hewitt

John R. Sweney

1. More a - bout Je - sus would I know, More of His grace to oth - ers show,
2. More a - bout Je - sus let me learn, More of His ho - ly will dis - cern;
3. More a - bout Je - sus in His Word Hold-ing com-mun-ion with my Lord,
4. More a - bout Je - sus on His throne, Riches in glo - ry all His own,

More of His sav - ing full - ness see, More of His love who died for me.
Spir - it of God, my teach - er be, Show-ing the things of Christ to me.
Hear-ing His voice in ev - 'ry line, Mak-ing each faith-ful say - ing mine.
More of His king-dom's sure increase, More of His com-ing—Prince of Peace.

CHORUS

More, more a - bout Je - sus, More, more a - bout Je - sus,

More of His sav - ing full - ness see, More of His love who died for me.

272 Wonderful Grace of Jesus

H. L.

Haldor Lillenas

1. Won-der-ful grace of Je-sus, Great-er than all my sin;......
2. Won-der-ful grace of Je-sus, Reach-ing to all the lost,....
3. Won-der-ful grace of Je-sus, Reach-ing the most de-filed,....

How shall my tongue de-scribe it, Where shall its praise be-gin?........
By it I have been par-doned, Saved to the ut-ter-most,........
By its trans-form-ing pow-er, Mak-ing him God's dear child,........

Tak-ing a-way my bur-den, Set-ting my spir-it free;...
Chains have been torn a-sun-der, Giv-ing me lib-er-ty;...
Pur-chas-ing peace and heav-en, For all e-ter-ni-ty;...

For the won-der-ful grace of Je-sus reach-es me.
For the won-der-ful grace of Je-sus reach-es me.
And the won-der-ful grace of Je-sus reach-es me.

CHORUS

the match-less grace of Je-sus,
Won-der-ful the matchless grace of Je - sus, Deep-er than the

273 Joy to the World!

Isaac Watts

George F. Handel

1. Joy to the world! the Lord is come; Let earth re-
2. Joy to the earth! the Sav - iour reigns; Let men their
3. No more let sins and sor - rows grow, Nor thorns in-
4. He rules the world with truth and grace, And makes the

ceive her King; Let ev - ery heart pre-pare Him room,
songs em - ploy; While fields and floods, rocks, hills and plains
fest the ground, He comes to make His bless - ings flow
na - tions prove The glo - ries of His right-eous - ness,

And heaven and na - ture sing, And heaven and na - ture
Re - peat the sound-ing joy, Re - peat the sound-ing
Far as the curse is found, Far as the curse is
And won - ders of His love, And won - ders of His
1. And heaven and na-ture sing, ... And

sing, And heaven, and heaven and na - ture sing.
joy, Re - peat, re - peat the sound-ing joy.
found, Far as, far as the curse is found.
love, And won-ders, and won - ders of His love.
heaven and na-ture sing,

It Came Upon the Midnight Clear   274

E. H. Sears

R. Storrs Willis

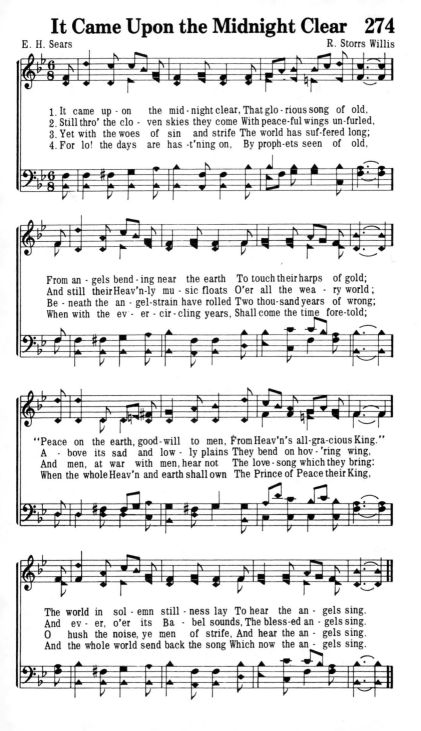

1. It came up-on the mid-night clear, That glo-rious song of old,
2. Still thro' the clo-ven skies they come With peace-ful wings un-furled,
3. Yet with the woes of sin and strife The world has suf-fered long;
4. For lo! the days are has-t'ning on, By proph-ets seen of old,

From an-gels bend-ing near the earth To touch their harps of gold;
And still their Heav'n-ly mu-sic floats O'er all the wea-ry world;
Be-neath the an-gel-strain have rolled Two thou-sand years of wrong;
When with the ev-er-cir-cling years, Shall come the time fore-told;

"Peace on the earth, good-will to men, From Heav'n's all-gra-cious King."
A-bove its sad and low-ly plains They bend on hov-'ring wing,
And men, at war with men, hear not The love-song which they bring:
When the whole Heav'n and earth shall own The Prince of Peace their King,

The world in sol-emn still-ness lay To hear the an-gels sing.
And ev-er, o'er its Ba-bel sounds, The bless-ed an-gels sing.
O hush the noise, ye men of strife, And hear the an-gels sing.
And the whole world send back the song Which now the an-gels sing.

275 Silent Night! Holy Night!

Joseph Mohr
Trans. by John F. Young

Franz Gruber

1. Si - lent night! ho - ly night! All is calm, all is bright Round yon vir-gin
2. Si - lent night! ho - ly night! Shepherds quake at the sight; Glories stream from
3. Si - lent night! ho - ly night! Son of God, love's pure light Radiant beams from

moth - er and Child, Ho - ly in - fant so ten - der and mild
heav - en a - far, Heav'n - ly hosts sing al - le - lu - ia
Thy ho - ly face With the dawn of re - deem - ing grace

Sleep in heav - en - ly peace, Sleep in heav - en - ly peace.
Christ, the Sav - ior is born! Christ, the Sav - ior is born.
Je - sus, Lord at Thy birth, Je - sus, Lord at Thy birth.

276 Away in a Manger

1-2 Anonymous
3 John T. McFarland

James R. Murray

1. A - way in a man - ger, No crib for a bed, The lit - tle Lord
2. The cat - tle are low - ing, The Ba - by a - wakes, But lit - tle Lord
3. Be near me, Lord Je - sus, I ask Thee to stay Close by me for-

Je - sus Laid down His sweet head; The stars in the sky Looked
Je - sus, No cry - ing He makes; I love Thee, Lord Je - sus! Look
ev - er, And love me, I pray; Bless all the dear chil-dren In

down where He lay, The lit - tle Lord Je - sus, A-sleep on the hay.
down from the sky, And stay by my cra - dle, Till morn-ing is nigh.
Thy ten - der care, And take us to Heav - en, To live with Thee there.

While Shepherds Watched Their Flocks 277

Nahum Tate

George F. Handel

1. While shep - herds watched their flocks by night, All seat - ed
2. "Fear not!" said He, for might - y dread Had seized the
3. To you, in Da - vid's town this day Is born, of
4. All glo - ry be to God on high, And to the

on the ground, The an - gel of the Lord came down,
trou - bled mind, Glad tid - ings of great joy I bring
Da - vid's line, The Sav - ior, who is Christ the Lord;
earth be peace; Good - will hence - forth from Heav'n to men,

And glo - ry shone a - round, And glo - ry shone a - round.
To you and all man - kind, To you and all man - kind.
And this shall be the sign: And this shall be the sign.
Be - gin and nev - er cease, Be - gin and nev - er cease.

278 Hark, the Herald Angels Sing

Charles Wesley

Felix Mendelssohn

1. Hark! the her - ald an - gels sing, "Glo - ry to the new-born King;
2. Christ, by high - est heaven a-dored; Christ, the ev - er - last-ing Lord:
3. Hail the heaven-born Prince of Peace! Hail the Sun of right-eous-ness!
4. Come, De - sire of na-tions, come! Fix in us Thy hum - ble home:

Peace on earth, and mer - cy mild; God and sin - ners rec - on-ciled."
Late in time be - hold Him come, Off-spring of a vir-gin's womb;
Light and life to all He brings, Risen with heal - ing in His wings:
Rise, the wom - an's conquering seed, Bruise in us the ser-pent's head;

Joy - ful, all ye na-tions, rise, Join the tri-umph of the skies;
Veiled in flesh the God-head see, Hail th' in - car-nate De - i - ty!
Mild He lays His glo - ry by, Born that man no more may die;
Ad - am's like-ness now ef - face, Stamp Thine im - age in its place:

With th' an - gel - ic hosts pro-claim, "Christ is born in Beth - le - hem."
Pleased as man with men t' ap-pear, Je - sus our Im - man-uel here.
Born to raise the sons of earth; Born to give them sec - ond birth.
Sec - ond Ad - am from a - bove, Re - in - state us in Thy love.

Hark! the her-ald an-gels sing, "Glo-ry to the new-born King."

O Come, All Ye Faithful 279

Latin Hymn
Trans. by Frederick Oakeley

From Wade's *Cantus Diversi*

1. O come, all ye faith - ful, joy - ful and tri - um-phant, Come ye, O
2. Sing, choirs of an - gels, sing in ex - ul - ta - tion, Sing, all ye
3. Yea, Lord, we greet Thee, born this hap-py morn-ing, Je - sus, to

come ye to Beth - le - hem; Come and be-hold Him,
bright hosts of Heav'n a - bove; Glo - ry to God, all
Thee be all glo - ry giv'n; Word of the Fa - ther,

CHORUS

born the King of an - gels:
glo - ry in the high - est: O come, let us a - dore Him, O come, let
now in flesh ap - pear - ing:

us a-dore Him, O come, let us a - dore Him, Christ, the Lord.

280 O Little Town of Bethlehem

Phillips Brooks

Lewis H. Redner

1. O lit - tle town of Beth - le - hem, How still we see thee lie!
2. For Christ is born of Ma - ry; And gath-ered all a - bove,
3. How si - lent - ly, how si - lent - ly The won-drous gift is giv'n,
4. O ho - ly Child of Beth - le - hem, De-scend to us, we pray;

A - bove thy deep and dream-less sleep The si - lent stars go by;
While mor-tals sleep the an - gels keep Their watch of won-d'ring love.
So God im - parts to hu - man hearts The bless-ings of His heav'n.
Cast out our sin and en - ter in, Be born in us to - day.

Yet in thy dark streets shin - eth The ev - er - last - ing Light;
O morn - ing stars, to - geth - er Pro-claim the ho - ly birth,
Nor ear may hear His com - ing; But in this world of sin,
We hear the Christ-mas an - gels The great glad ti - dings tell,

The hopes and fears of all the years Are met in Thee to - night.
And prais - es sing to God the King, And peace to men on earth.
Where meek souls will re - ceive Him still, The dear Christ en - ters in.
O come to us, a - bide with us, Our Lord Em - man - u - el.

Battle Hymn of the Republic 281

Julia Ward Howe

William Steffe

1. Mine eyes have seen the glo - ry of the com - ing of the Lord;
2. I have seen Him in the watch-fires of a hun-dred cir-cling camps;
3. He has sound-ed forth the trum - pets that shall nev - er sound re-treat;
4. In the beau - ty of the lil - ies Christ was born a-cross the sea,

He is tramp-ling out the vin-tage where the grapes of wrath are stored;
They have build-ed Him an al - tar in the eve-ning dews and damps;
He is sift - ing out the hearts of men be - fore His judg-ment seat;
With a glo - ry in His bos - om that trans-fig-ures you and me;

He hath loosed the fate-ful light-ning of His ter - ri - ble swift sword;
I can read His right-eous sen-tence by His dim and flar - ing lamps;
O be swift my soul to an - swer Him! be ju - bi - lant, my feet!
As He died to make men ho - ly let us die to make men free;

CHORUS

His truth is march-ing on. Glo-ry, glo-ry, hal-le-lu - jah, Glo-ry, glo-ry

hal - le - lu-jah, Glo-ry, glo-ry, hal - le-lu-jah, His truth is march-ing on.

282 The Star Spangled Banner

Francis Scott Key

Attributed to John Stafford Smith

1. Oh, say, can you see by the dawn's ear - ly light, What so
2. Oh, thus be it ev - er when free men shall stand Be -

proud - ly we hailed at the twi - light's last gleam - ing, Whose broad
tween their loved homes and the war's des - o - la - tion! Blest with

stripes and bright stars, thro' the per - il - ous fight, O'er the ram - parts we watched,
vic't'ry and peace, may the Heav'n res - cued land Praise the Pow'r that hath made

were so gal - lant - ly stream - ing? And the rock - ets' red glare, the bombs
and pre - served us a na - tion! Then con - quer we must, when our

burst - ing in air Gave proof thro' the night that our flag was still there,
cause it is just, And this be our mot - to: "In God is our trust!"

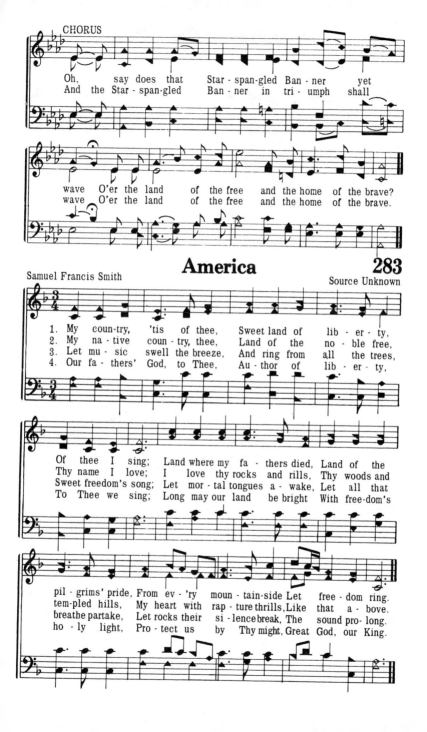

CHORUS

Oh, say does that Star-spangled Ban-ner yet
And the Star-spangled Ban-ner in tri-umph shall

wave O'er the land of the free and the home of the brave?
wave O'er the land of the free and the home of the brave.

America 283

Samuel Francis Smith

Source Unknown

1. My coun-try, 'tis of thee, Sweet land of lib-er-ty,
2. My na-tive coun-try, thee, Land of the no-ble free,
3. Let mu-sic swell the breeze, And ring from all the trees,
4. Our fa-thers' God, to Thee, Au-thor of lib-er-ty,

Of thee I sing; Land where my fa-thers died, Land of the
Thy name I love; I love thy rocks and rills, Thy woods and
Sweet freedom's song; Let mor-tal tongues a-wake, Let all that
To Thee we sing; Long may our land be bright With free-dom's

pil-grims' pride, From ev-'ry moun-tain-side Let free-dom ring.
tem-pled hills, My heart with rap-ture thrills, Like that a-bove.
breathe partake, Let rocks their si-lence break, The sound pro-long.
ho-ly light, Pro-tect us by Thy might, Great God, our King.

284 America the Beautiful!

Katherine Lee Bates

Samuel A. Ward

1. O beau-ti-ful for spa-cious skies, For amber waves of grain,
2. O beau-ti-ful for pil-grim feet, Whose stern, impassioned stress
3. O beau-ti-ful for heroes proved In lib-er-at-ting strife,
4. O beau-ti-ful for pa-triot dream That sees be-yond the years,

For pur-ple moun-tain maj-es-ties A-bove the fruit-ed plain!
A thor-ough-fare for free-dom beat A-cross the wil-der-ness!
Who more than self their coun-try loved, And mer-cy more than life!
Thine al-a-bas-ter cit-ies gleam, Undimmed by hu-man tears!

A-mer-i-ca! A-mer-i-ca! God shed His grace on thee,
A-mer-i-ca! A-mer-i-ca! God mend thine ev-'ry flaw,
A-mer-i-ca! A-mer-i-ca! May God thy gold re-fine,
A-mer-i-ca! A-mer-i-ca! God shed His grace on thee,

And crown thy good with broth-er-hood From sea to shin-ing sea!
Con-firm thy soul in self-control, Thy lib-er-ty in law!
Till all suc-cess be no-ble-ness, And ev-'ry gain di-vine!
And crown thy good with broth-er-hood From sea to shin-ing sea!

Responsive Readings

285 Adoration

Psalms 8

O Lord our Lord, how excellent is thy name in all the earth!

Who hast set thy glory above the heavens.

Out of the mouth of babes and sucklings hast thou ordained strength because of thine enemies, that thou mightest still the enemy and the avenger.

When I consider thy heavens, the work of thy fingers, the moon and the stars, which thou hast ordained;

What is man, that thou art mindful of him? and the son of man, that thou visitest him?

For thou hast made him a little lower than the angels, and hast crowned him with glory and honour.

Thou madest him to have dominion over the works of thy hands; thou hast put all things under his feet:

All sheep and oxen, yea, and the beasts of the field;

The fowl of the air, and the fish of the sea, and whatsoever passeth through the paths of the seas.

O Lord our Lord, how excellent is thy name in all the earth!

286 Praise

Psalms 96: 1-10

O sing unto the Lord a new song: sing unto the Lord, all the earth.

Sing unto the Lord, bless his name; shew forth his salvation from day to day.

Declare his glory among the heathen, his wonders among all people.

For the Lord is great, and greatly to be praised: he is to be feared above all gods.

For all the gods of the nations are idols: but the Lord made the heavens.

Honour and majesty are before him: strength and beauty are in his sanctuary.

Give unto the Lord, O ye kindreds of the people, give unto the Lord glory and strength.

Give unto the Lord the glory due unto his name: bring an offering, and come into his courts.

O worship the Lord in the beauty of holiness: fear before him, all the earth.

Say among the heathen that the Lord reigneth: the world also shall be established that it shall not be moved: he shall judge the people righteously.

Now faith is the substance of things hoped for, the evidence of things not seen.

By faith Abel offered unto God a more excellent sacrifice than Cain, by which he obtained witness that he was righteous, God testifying of his gifts: and by it he being dead yet speaketh.

By faith Enoch was translated that he should not see death; and was not found, because God had translated him: for before his translation he had this testimony, that he pleased God.

But without faith it is impossible to please him: for he that cometh to God must believe that he is, and that he is a rewarder of them that diligently seek him.

By faith Noah, being warned of God of things not seen as yet, moved with fear, prepared an ark to the saving of his house; by the which he condemned the world, and became heir of the righteousness which is by faith.

By faith Abraham, when he was called to go out into a place which he should after receive for an inheritance, obeyed; and he went out, not knowing whither he went.

By faith he sojourned in the land of promise, as in a strange country, dwelling in tabernacles with Isaac and Jacob, the heirs with him of the same promise:

For he looked for a city which hath foundations, whose builder and maker is God.

Though I speak with the tongues of men and of angels, and have not charity, I am become as sounding brass, or a tinkling cymbal.

And though I have the gift of prophecy, and understand all mysteries, and all knowledge; and though I have all faith, so that I could remove mountains, and have not charity, I am nothing.

And though I bestow all my goods to feed the poor, and though I give my body to be burned, and have not charity, it profiteth me nothing.

Charity suffereth long, and is kind; charity envieth not; charity vaunteth not itself, is not puffed up,

Doth not behave itself unseemly, seeketh not her own, is not easily provoked, thinketh no evil;

Rejoiceth not in iniquity, but rejoiceth in the truth;

Beareth all things, believeth all things, hopeth all things, endureth all things.

Charity never faileth: but whether there be prophecies, they shall fail; whether there be tongues, they shall cease; whether there be knowledge, it shall vanish away.

For we know in part, and we prophesy in part. But when that which is perfect is come, then that which is in part shall be done away.

When I was a child, I spake as a child, I understood as a child, I thought as a child: but when I became a man, I put away childish things.

For now we see through a glass darkly; but then face to face: now I know in part; but then shall I know even as also I am known.

And I will pray the Father, and he shall give you another Comforter, that he may abide with you for ever;

Even the Spirit of truth; whom the world cannot receive, because it seeth him not, neither knoweth him: but ye know him; for he dwelleth with you, and shall be in you.

But the Comforter, which is the Holy Ghost, whom the Father will send in my name, he shall teach you all things, and bring all things to your remembrance, whatsoever I have said unto you.

Nevertheless I tell you the truth; It is expedient for you that I go away: for if I go not away, the Comforter will not come unto you; but if I depart, I will send him unto you.

And when he is come, he will reprove the world of sin, and of righteousness, and of judgment:

Of sin, because they believe not on me;

Of righteousness, because I go to my Father, and ye see me no more;

Of judgment, because t h e prince of this world is judged.

I have yet many things to say unto you, but ye cannot bear them now.

Howbeit when he, the Spirit of truth, is come, he will guide you into all truth: for he shall not speak of himself; but whatsoever he shall hear, that shall he speak: and he will shew you things to come.

He shall glorify me: for he shall receive of mine, and shall shew it unto you.

After this manner therefore pray ye: Our Father which art in heaven, Hallowed be thy name.

Thy kingdom come. Thy will be done in earth, as it is in heaven.

Give us this day our daily bread.

And forgive us our debts, as we forgive our debtors.

And lead us not into temptation, but deliver us from evil: For thine is the kingdom, and the power, and the glory, for ever. Amen.

For if ye forgive men their trespasses, your heavenly Father will also forgive you:

But if ye forgive not men their trespasses, neither will your Father forgive your trespasses.

Ask, and it shall be given you; seek, and ye shall find; knock, and it shall be opened unto you:

For every one that asketh receiveth; and he that seeketh findeth; and to him that knocketh it shall be opened.

Or what man is there of you, whom if his son ask bread, will he give him a stone? Or if he ask a fish, will he give him a serpent?

If ye then, being evil, know how to give good gifts unto your children, how much more shall your Father which is in heaven give good things to them that ask him?

The effectual fervent prayer of a righteous man availeth much.

Exodus 20: 3-5a, 7-8, 12-17; Matthew 22: 36-39

Matthew 24: 45-47; Luke 16: 10-13; Revelation 2: 10b; I Corinthians 15: 57-58

Thou shalt have no other gods before me.

Thou shalt not make unto thee any graven image, or any likeness of any thing that is in heaven above, or that is in the earth beneath, or that is in the water under the earth: Thou shalt not bow down thyself to them, nor serve them:

Thou shalt not take the name of the Lord thy God in vain; for the Lord will not hold him guiltless that taketh his name in vain.

Remember the sabbath day, to keep it holy.

Honour thy father and thy mother: that thy days may be long upon the land which the Lord thy God giveth thee.

Thou shalt not kill.

Thou shalt not commit adultery.

Thou shalt not steal.

Thou shalt not bear false witness against thy neighbour.

Thou shalt not covet.

Master, which is the great commandment in the law?

Jesus said unto him, Thou shalt love the Lord thy God with all thy heart, and with all thy soul, and with all thy mind.

This is the first and great commandment.

And the second is like unto it, Thou shalt love thy neighbour as thyself.

Who then is a faithful and wise servant, whom his lord hath made ruler over his household, to give them meat in due season?

Blessed is that servant, whom his lord when he cometh shall find so doing.

Verily I say unto you, That he shall make him ruler over all his goods.

He that is faithful in that which is least is faithful also in much: and he that is unjust in the least is unjust also in much.

If therefore ye have not been faithful in the unrighteous mammon, who will commit to your trust the true riches?

And if ye have not been faithful in that which is another man's, who shall give you that which is your own?

No servant can serve two masters: for either he will hate the one, and love the other; or else he will hold to the one, and despise the other. Ye cannot serve God and mammon.

Be thou faithful unto death, and I will give thee a crown of life.

Thanks be to God, which giveth us the victory through our Lord Jesus Christ.

Therefore, my beloved brethren, be ye stedfast, unmovable, always abounding in the work of the Lord, forasmuch as ye know that your labour is not in vain in the Lord.

The people that walked in darkness have seen a great light:

They that dwell in the land of the shadow of death, upon them hath the light shined.

Thou hast multiplied the nation, and not increased the joy:

They joy before thee according to the joy in harvest, and as men rejoice when they divide the spoil.

For thou hast broken the yoke of his burden, and the staff of his shoulder, the rod of his oppressor, as in the day of Midian.

For every battle of the warrior is with confused noise, and garments rolled in blood; but this shall be with burning and fuel of fire.

For unto us a child is born, unto us a son is given: and the government shall be upon his shoulder:

And his name shall be called W o n d e r f u l, Counsellor, The mighty God, The everlasting Father, The Prince of Peace.

Of the increase of his government and peace there shall be no end, upon the throne of David, and upon his kingdom, to order it, and to establish it with judgment and with justice from henceforth even for ever.

The zeal of the Lord of hosts will perform this.

The Lord himself shall give you a sign;

Behold, a virgin shall conceive, and bear a son, and shall call his name Immanuel.

And she brought forth her firstborn son, and wrapped him in swaddling clothes, and laid him in a manger; because there was no room for them in the inn.

And there were in the same country shepherds abiding in the field, keeping watch over their flock by night.

And, lo, the angel of the Lord came upon them, and the glory of the Lord shone round about them: and they were sore afraid.

And the angel said unto them, Fear not: for, behold, I bring you good tidings of great joy, which shall be to all people.

For unto you is born this day in the city of David a Saviour, which is Christ the Lord.

And this shall be a sign unto you; Ye shall find the babe wrapped in swaddling clothes, lying in a manger.

And suddenly there was with the angel a multitude of the heavenly host praising God, and saying,

Glory to God in the highest, and on earth peace, good will toward men.

And it came to pass, as the angels were gone away from them into heaven, the shepherds said one to another, Let us now go even unto Bethlehem, and see this thing which is come to pass.

And they came with haste, and found Mary, and Joseph, and the babe lying in a manger.

Come unto me, all ye that labour and are heavy laden, and I will give you rest.

Take my yoke upon you, and learn of me; for I am meek and lowly in heart:

And ye shall find rest unto your souls.

For my yoke is easy, and my burden is light.

Ho, every one that thirsteth, come ye to the waters, and he that hath no money; come ye, buy, and eat; yea, come, buy wine and milk without money and without price.

Wherefore do ye spend money for that which is not bread? and your labour for that which satisfieth not? hearken diligently unto me, and eat ye that which is good, and let your soul delight itself in fatness.

Incline your ear, and come unto me: hear, and your soul shall live; and I will make an everlasting covenant with you, even the sure mercies of David.

All that the Father giveth me shall come to me: and him that cometh to me I will in no wise cast out.

For I came down from heaven, not to do mine own will, but the will of him that sent me.

And this is the will of him that sent me, that every one which seeth the Son, and believeth on him, may have everlasting life: and I will raise him up at the last day.

And as Moses lifted up the serpent in the wilderness, even so must the Son of man be lifted up:

That whosoever believeth in him should not perish, but have eternal life.

For God so loved the world, that he gave his only begotten Son, that whosoever believeth in him should not perish, but have everlasting life.

For God sent not his Son into the world to condemn the world; but that the world through him might be saved.

He that believeth on him is not condemned: but he that believeth not is condemned already, because he hath not believed in the name of the only begotten Son of God.

And this is the condemnation, that light is come into the world, and men loved darkness rather than light, because their deeds were evil.

For every one that doeth evil hateth the light, neither cometh to the light, lest his deeds should be reproved.

But he that doeth truth cometh to the light, that his deeds may be made manifest, that they are wrought in God.

These are written, that ye might believe that Jesus is the Christ, the Son of God;

And that believing ye might have life through his name.

Blessed are the poor in spirit: for theirs is the kingdom of heaven.

Blessed are they that mourn: for they shall be comforted.

Blessed are the meek: for they shall inherit the earth.

Blessed are they which do hunger and thirst after righteousness: for they shall be filled.

Blessed are the merciful: for they shall obtain mercy.

Blessed are the pure in heart for they shall see God.

Blessed are the peacemakers: for they shall be called the children of God.

Blessed are they which are persecuted for righteousness' sake: for theirs is the kingdom of heaven.

Blessed are ye, when men shall revile you, and persecute you, and shall say all manner of evil against you falsely, for my sake.

Rejoice, and be exceeding glad: for great is your reward in heaven: for so persecuted they the prophets which were before you.

Ye are the salt of the earth: but if the salt have lost his savour, wherewith shall it be salted? it is thenceforth good for nothing, but to be cast out, and to be trodden under foot of men.

Ye are the light of the world. A city that is set on an hill cannot be hid.

Let your light so shine before men, that they may see your good works, and glorify your Father which is in heaven.

After this I beheld, and, lo, a great multitude, which no man could number, of all nations, and kindreds, and people, and tongues, stood before the throne, and before the Lamb, clothed with white robes, and palms in their hands;

And cried with a loud voice, saying, Salvation to our God which sitteth upon the throne, and unto the Lamb.

And all the angels stood round about the throne, and about the elders and the four beasts, and fell before the throne on their faces, and worshipped God,

Saying, Amen: Blessing, and glory, and wisdom, and thanksgiving, and honour, and power, and might, be unto our God for ever and ever. Amen.

And one of the elders answered, saying unto me, What are these which are arrayed in white robes? and whence came they?

And I said unto him, Sir, thou knowest. And he said to me, These are they which came out of great tribulation, and h a v e washed their robes, and made them white in the blood of the Lamb.

Therefore are they before the throne of God, and serve him day and night in his temple: and he that sitteth on the throne shall dwell among them.

For the Lamb which is in the midst of the throne shall feed them, and shall lead them unto living fountains of waters: and God shall wipe away all tears from their eyes.

299 My Light

Psalms 27: 1-11, 13-14

The Lord is my light and my salvation; whom shall I fear? the Lord is the strength of my life; of whom shall I be afraid?

When the wicked, even mine enemies and my foes, came upon me to eat up my flesh, they stumbled and fell.

Though an host should encamp against me, my heart shall not fear: though war should rise against me, in this will I be confident.

One thing have I desired of the Lord, that will I seek after;

That I may dwell in the house of the Lord all the days of my life, to behold the beauty of the Lord, and to enquire in his temple.

For in the time of trouble he shall hide me in his pavilion:

In the secret of his tabernacle shall he hide me; he shall set me up upon a rock.

And now shall mine head be lifted up above mine enemies round about me:

Therefore will I offer in his tabernacle sacrifices of joy; I will sing, yea, I will sing praises unto the Lord.

Hear, O Lord, when I cry with my voice: have mercy also upon me, and answer me.

When thou saidst, Seek ye my face; my heart said unto thee, Thy face, Lord, will I seek.

Hide not thy face far from me; put not thy servant away in anger: thou hast been my help; leave me not, neither forsake me, O God of my salvation.

When my father and my mother forsake me, then the Lord will take me up.

Teach me thy way, O Lord, and lead me in a plain path, because of mine enemies.

I had fainted, unless I had believed to see the goodness of the Lord in the land of the living.

Wait on the Lord: be of good courage, and he shall strengthen thine heart: wait I say, on the Lord.

300 My Help

Psalms 121

I will lift up mine eyes unto the hills, from whence cometh my help.

My help cometh from the Lord, which made heaven and earth.

He will not suffer thy foot to be moved: he that keepeth thee will not slumber.

Behold, he that keepeth Israel shall neither slumber nor sleep.

The Lord is thy keeper: the Lord is thy shade upon thy right hand.

The sun shall not smite thee by day, nor the moon by night.

The Lord shall preserve thee from all evil: he shall preserve thy soul.

The Lord shall preserve thy going out and thy coming in from this time forth, and even for evermore.

The Lord is my shepherd; I shall not want.

He maketh me to lie down in green pastures: he leadeth me beside the still waters.

He restoreth my soul: he leadeth me in the paths of righteousness for his name's sake.

Yea, though I walk through the valley of the shadow of death, I will fear no evil: for thou art with me; thy rod and thy staff they comfort me.

Thou preparest a table before me in the presence of mine enemies: thou anointest my head with oil; my cup runneth over.

Surely goodness and mercy shall follow me all the days of my life: and I will dwell in the house of the Lord for ever.

I am the good shepherd: the good shepherd giveth his life for the sheep. . . . I am the good shepherd, and know my sheep, and am known of mine.

As the Father knoweth me, even so know I the Father: and I lay down my life for the sheep.

And other sheep I have, which are not of this fold: them also I must bring, and they shall hear my voice; and there shall be one fold, and one shepherd.

Therefore doth my Father love me, because I lay down my life, that I might take it again.

And he arose out of the synagogue, and entered into Simon's house.

And Simon's wife's mother was taken with a great fever; and they besought him for her.

And he stood over her, and rebuked the fever; and it left her: and immediately she arose and ministered unto them.

Now when the sun was setting, all they that had any sick with divers diseases brought them unto him;

And he laid his hands on every one of them, and healed them.

And as he entered into a certain village, there met him ten men that were lepers, which stood afar off:

And they lifted up their voices, and said, Jesus, Master, have mercy on us.

And when he saw them, he said unto them, Go shew yourselves unto the priests. And it came to pass, that, as they went, they were cleansed.

And one of them, when he saw that he was healed, turned back, and with a loud voice glorified God,

And fell down on his face at his feet, giving him thanks: and he was a Samaritan.

And Jesus answering said, Were there not ten cleansed? but where are the nine?

And he said unto him, Arise, go thy way: thy faith hath made thee whole.

Benedictions

The Lord bless thee and keep thee: The Lord make
his face shine upon thee, and be gracious unto thee:
the Lord lift up his countenance upon thee,
and give thee peace. Amen.
Numbers 6:24, 26

Now the God of peace, that brought again from the
dead our Lord Jesus Christ, that great Shepherd of the
sheep, through the blood of the everlasting covenants,
make you perfect in every good to do his will,
working in you that which is wellpleasing in his sight,
through Jesus Christ; to whom he glory for ever
and ever. Amen.
Hebrews 13:20, 21

Now our Lord Jesus Christ himself, and God, even
our Father, which hath loved us, and hath given us
everlasting consolation and good hope through grace,
Comfort your hearts and stablish you in every
good word and work. Amen.
II Thessalonians 2:16, 17

Now unto him that is able to keep you from falling,
and to present you faultless before the presence of his
glory with exceding joy, to the only wise God our Savior
be glory and majesty, dominion and power,
both now and ever. Amen.
Jude 24, 25

The grace of our Lord Jesus Christ be with your
spirit. Amen.
Philemon 25

COMPLETE TOPICAL INDEX

This Cross Index will assist in planning religious services. The appropriate song for any occasion, or for any subject can easily be selected.

ACTIVITY

A Beautiful Life 121
Bring All Your Needs to the Altar 38
Bringing In the Sheaves 31
He Keeps Me Singing 53
Higher Ground 220
I Am Bound for the Promised Land 97
I Feel Like Traveling On 152
I'm In This Church 210
Just a Closer Walk 208
Learning to Lean 36
Light the Light 135
Living By Faith 151
Looking For a City 187
Onward, Christian Soldiers 254
Press Along to Gloryland 120
Rescue the Perishing 261
Showing My Appreciation 96
The Glove 182
Trust and Obey 2
We'll Work Till Jesus Comes 205
Work for the Night is Coming 224

ASSURANCE AND TRUST

All in the Name of Jesus 47
Blessed Assurance 27
Each Step I Take 6
Give Them All to Jesus 48
Hand in Hand with Jesus 29
He Will Pilot Me 175
He's As Close As the Mention of His Name 49
He's With Me Always 203
Hold to God's Unchanging Hand 162
I Need Thee Every Hour 249
I Stand Upon the Rock of Ages 94
I Won't Have to Cross Jordan Alone 58
I'll Have a New Life 173
I'll Live in Glory 149
I'm Standing On the Solid Rock 40
I've Got a Reservation 111
Just a Little Talk with Jesus 178
Learning to Lean 36
Living By Faith 151
My Faith Looks Up to Thee 107
Only Trust Him 84
Redemption Draweth Nigh 77
The Brush 168
The Last Mile of the Way 57
The Unseen Hand 197
Through It All 79
'Tis So Sweet to Trust in Jesus 268
Trust and Obey 2
What a Friend 88
What a Precious Friend 228
When It's Time 146
Where Could I Go? 43
Without a Doubt I'm Saved 193
Yes, I Know 221

ATONEMENT

Amazing Grace 37
At Calvary 21
At the Cross 23
Hallelujah for the Cross 244
Hallelujah, What a Savior! 242
He Looked Beyond My Fault 102
I Gave My Life for Thee 235
I Should Have Been Crucified 157
I Will Glory in the Cross 81
If That Isn't Love 22
Innocent Blood 98
Jesus Paid It All 82
Kneel at the Cross 209
Lonely Road Up Calvary's Way 17
Love Grew Where the Blood Fell 165

Love is Why 68
Love Lifted Me 9
Nailing My Sins to His Cross 83
Nothing But the Blood 240
One Day 246
Redeemed 123
Rise and Be Healed 18
Room at the Cross for You 14
Ten Thousand Angels 75
The Blood That Stained the 140
The Healer 252
There is a Fountain 222
Where You There? 207
What a Savior 65
What Did He Do? 243
What Sins Are You Talkin' About? 93
When I See the Blood 63
When I Survey the Wondrous Cross 80
When The Savior Reached Down for Me ... 66

BLOOD (See Atonement)

CHILDREN'S SONGS

Away in a Manger 276
Greater Is He That Is In Me 248
Holy Bible, Book Divine 174
Jesus Loves Me 213
Lift Him Up 3
Surely Goodness and Mercy 89
The Fire Song 215
The Old-Time Religion 237
We Will Rise and Shine 206
Whisper a Prayer 143

CHOIR SPECIALS

All in the Name of Jesus 47
Bring All Your Needs 38
Each Step I Take 6
Fill My Cup, Lord 13
Hallelujah for the Cross 244
Holy Spirit, Thou Art Welcome 109
I'm Standing on the Solid Rock 40
Jesus (He is the Son of God) 52
Love Grew Where the Blood Fell 165
Redemption Draweth Nigh 77
Rise and Be Healed 18
Room at the Cross for You 14
Sound the Battle Cry 115
Surely Goodness and Mercy 89
Ten Thousand Years 69
The Healer 252
The Savior Is Waiting 230
There's a Whole Lot of People 137
Through It All 79
Touring That City 112
Wonderful Grace of Jesus 272

CHRISTMAS

Away In a Manger 276
O Come All Ye Faithful 279
O Little Town of Bethlehem 280
Hark the Herald Angels Sing 278
It Came Upon the Midnight Clear 274
Joy to the World 273
Silent Night 275
While Shepherds Watched Their 277

CLOSING SONGS

Blest Be the Tie 145
God Be With You 54
God's Wonderful People 50
How Great Thou Art 4
Surely Goodness and Mercy 89
To God Be the Glory 26

CONSECRATION

Close to Thee 195
Closer to You 142
Consider the Lilies 51
Have Thine Own Way, Lord 90
He Looked Beyond My Fault 102
I Am Resolved 10
I'll Be a Friend to Jesus 153
I've Never Loved Him Better 227
Jesus, I Come 260
Just a Closer Walk 208
Just As I Am 45
Learning to Lean 36
Look for Me at Jesus's Feet 167
Must Jesus Bear the Cross Alone 101
My Jesus, I Love Thee 122
O Master, Let Me Walk with Thee 99
Open my Eyes 129
Safe in the Arms of Jesus 258
Showing my Appreciation 96
Take Time to Be Holy 70
The Glove 182
The Brush 168
We'll Work Till Jesus Comes 205

CONSOLATION

Asleep in Jesus 192
Bring All Your Needs 38
Do You Know my Jesus? 61
Does Jesus Care? 56
Each Step I Take 6
Give Them All to Jesus 48
He Hideth My Soul 259
He's As Close as the Mention 49
He's With Me Always 203
Hiding in Thee 78
Hold to God's Unchanging Hand 162
How Beautiful Heaven Must Be 35
How Great Thou Art 4
I Won't Have to Cross Jordan 58
I'll See You in the Rapture 114
If We Never Meet Again 110
Learning to Lean 36
Mansion Over the Hilltop 15
No Tears in Heaven 251
Rock of Ages 1
Sweet By and By 264
Tears Will Never Stain the 87
Ten Thousand Years 69
That Glad Reunion Day 139
The Eastern Gate 201
The Last Mile of the Way 57
The Unseen Hand 197
The Way That He Loves 16
There's a Whole Lot of People 137
These Are They 148
This is Just What Heaven Means 219
Through It All 79
'Tis So Sweet to Trust in Jesus 268
What a Day That Will Be 30
What a Precious Friend 228
When My Feet Touch the Streets 216
When That Old Ship of Zion 189
When the Roll is Called 67
When They Ring the Golden Bells 64
Where the Roses Never Fade 92
Where We'll Never Grow Old 169
Whispering Hope 34
Won't it be Wonderful There? 155

CROSS (See Atonement)

DEVOTION, PRAISE AND WORSHIP

All Hail the Power 76
Blessed Assurance 27
Doxology 186
God's Wonderful People 50
Hand in Hand with Jesus 29
He Keeps Me Singing 53
Holy Spirit, Thou Art 109
How Great Thou Art 4
I'll Be a Friend to Jesus 153
I've Never Loved Him Better 227
Jesus is the Sweetest Name 7
My Jesus, I Love Thee 122
O Master, Let Me Walk 99
O Worship the King 200
Praise Him! Praise Him! 269
Rejoice, Ye Pure in Heart 241
Showing my Appreciation 96
Statue of Liberty 24
Thank God, I Am Free 136
The Way That He Loves 16
There Is a Name 179
To God Be the Glory 26
We Thank Thee, Lord 133
What a Savior 65
Somebody Loves Me 190

FRIEND

Blest Be the Tie 145
God's Wonderful People 50
I Learned About Jesus 108
I'll Be a Friend to Jesus 153
Just a Little Talk with 178
No, Not One 74
The Way That He Loves 16
What a Friend 88
What a Precious Friend 228
Where Could I Go? 43

GRATITUDE AND THANKSGIVING

Amazing Grace 37
Count Your Blessings 20
Doxology 186
Glory to His Name 238
Hallelujah for the Cross 244
How Great Thou Art 4
Joy Unspeakable 8
Showing My Appreciation 96
We Thank Thee, Lord 133

HEAVEN

A Song Holy Angels Cannot 91
Beautiful Isle 19
Caught Up Together 211
Glory Road 177
Heaven For Me 100
How Beautiful Heaven Must Be 35
I Want to Be Ready to Meet 138
I'll Have a New Life 173
I'll Live in Glory 149
I'll Meet You by the River 144
I'll Meet You in the Morning 163
I'll See You in the Rapture 114
I've Got a Reservation 111
I've Never Been This Homesick 128
If We Never Meet Again 110
It Made News in Heaven 44
Jesus Will Outshine Them All 71
Just Over in the Glory Land 119
Life's Railway to Heaven 225
Look for Me at Jesus' Feet 167
Looking for a City 187
Mansion Over the Hilltop 15
Meet Me There 73
No Tears in Heaven 251
O I Want to See Him 117
Queen of Paradise 184
Shall We Gather at the River 5
Supper Time 116
Sweet By and By 264
Tears Will Never Stain 87
Ten Thousand Years 69
That Glad Reunion Day 139
The Eastern Gate 210
The Glory Land Way 170
The Old Gospel Ship 214
There's a Whole Lot of People 137
There's Coming a Day 196
These Are They 148
This is Just What Heaven Means 219
Touring That City 112
What a Day That Will Be 30
When It's Time 146

When My Feet Touch the Streets 216
When That Old Ship of Zion 189
When the Roll is Called Up 67
When They Ring the Golden 64
Where the Roses Never Fade 92
Where We'll Never Grow Old 169
Won't It Be Wonderful There? 155

INVITATION

Almost Persuaded 86
Bring All Your Needs to 38
Do You Know my Jesus? 61
Have Thine Own Way, Lord 90
I Am Coming to the Cross 239
I Am Resolved 10
I Gave my Life for Thee 235
Jesus Calls Us 172
Jesus, I Come 260
Jesus is Calling 231
Jesus Paid It All 82
Just As I Am 45
Kneel at the Cross 209
Lord, I'm Coming Home 233
Only Trust Him 84
Pass Me Not 236
Room at the Cross for You 14
The Savior is Waiting 230
The Time is Now 229
There is a Fountain 222
Trust and Obey 2
Where He Leads Me 247
Why Not Now? 124

JESUS

All in the Name of Jesus 47
Do You Know my Jesus? 61
Hand in Hand with Jesus 29
He's as Close as the Mention 49
I'll be a Friend to Jesus 153
Jesus (He is the Son of God) 52
Jesus is the Sweetest Name 7
Jesus, Lover of my Soul 226
Jesus Will Outshine Them All 71
Just a Little Talk with Jesus 178
Lift Him Up 3
More About Jesus 271
My Jesus, I Love Thee 122
No, Not One 74
Only Jesus Can Satisfy 104
The Carpenter from Nazareth 188
The Healer 252
'Tis So Sweet to Trust in Jesus 268
Victory in Jesus 159
What a Friend 88
What a Precious Friend 228

JOY

Blessed Assurance 27
Give Them All to Jesus 48
He Keeps Me Singing 53
I'm Free Again 134
It Made News in Heaven 44
It's Different Now 180
Joy to the World 273
Joy Unspeakable 8
Light the Light 135
Press Along to Gloryland 120
Rejoice, Ye Pure in Heart 241
Ring the Bells of Heaven 267
That Glad Reunion Day 139
Way Down Deep in my Soul 161
When God Dips His Love in 130

LOVE

Heavenly Love 147
I've Never Loved Him Better 227
If That Isn't Love 22
Jesus Loves Even Me 105
Jesus Loves Me 213
Love Grew Where the Blood 165
Love is Why 68

Love Lifted Me 9
My Jesus, I Love Thee 122
My Savior's Love 55
Somebody Loves Me 190
The Way That He Loves 16
There Is a Name 179
When God Dips His Love in 130
Wonderful Love 113

LOYALTY

Blest Be the Tie 145
Bringing in the Sheaves 31
Closer to You 142
Footsteps of Jesus 39
Higher Ground 220
Hold to God's Unchanging 162
I Am Resolved 10
I Feel Like Traveling 152
I Would Not Be Denied 72
I'll Be a Friend to Jesus 153
I'm in This Church 210
I'm Standing on the Solid 40
I've Never Loved Him 227
Jesus Calls Us 172
Just a Closer Walk 208
Learning to Lean 36
Light the Light 135
Must Jesus Bear the Cross 101
My Faith Looks Up to Thee 107
O Master, Let Me Walk 99
Onward, Christian Soldiers 254
Press Along to Gloryland 120
Send the Light 263
Sound the Battle Cry 115
Statue of Liberty 24
These Are They 148
Through It All 79
Trust and Obey 2
We'll Work Till Jesus 205
When I Survey the 80
Where He Leads Me 247
Work for the Night is 224

PATRIOTIC

America 283
America, the Beautiful 284
Battle Hymn of the Republic 281
Statue of Liberty 24
The Star-Spangled Banner 282

PEACE

All in the Name of Jesus 47
Learning to Lean 36
Only Jesus Can Satisfy 104
Redemption Draweth Nigh 77
This is Just What Heaven 219

PENTECOST AND THE HOLY SPIRIT

Everytime I Feel the 218
Greater is He That is 248
Holy Spirit, Thou Art 109
Old-Time Power 126
Revive Us Again 131

PETITION AND PRAYER

Bring All Your Needs 38
Closer to You 142
Did You Think to Pray? 181
Fill My Cup, Lord 13
Have Thine Own Way, Lord 90
He's As Close As the 49
Hear Our Prayer, O Lord 103
Hide Me, Rock of Ages 141
Hide Thou Me 85
In the Garden 12
Jesus, Have Mercy On Me 164
O Master, Let Me Walk 99
Open My Eyes 129
Pass Me Not 236
The Glove 182

QUARTET SONGS

A Beautiful Life 121
Each Step I Take 6
Heaven For Me 100
How Great Thou Art 4
I'll Meet You in the Morning 163
I'm Standing On the Solid 40
I've Got a Reservation 111
If We Never Meet Again 110
Jesus Hold My Hand 166
Just a Little Talk 178
Mansion Over the Hilltop 15
Redemption Draweth Nigh 77
Rise And Be Healed 18
Room At the Cross 14
Ten Thousand Years 69
The Healer 252
Touring That City 112
Victory in Jesus 159
What a Day That Will Be 30
What Sins Are You Talkin' 93

REDEMPTION (See Atonement)

REVIVAL

Bringing in the Sheaves 31
Come and Dine 32
Higher Ground 220
I Came On Business for 42
I Can Tell You the 127
Lift Him Up 3
Love Lifted Me 9
Open My Eyes 129
Rescue the Perishing 261
Revive Us Again 131
Send the Light 263
The Brush 168
Throw Out the Life-line 262
We'll Work Till Jesus 205
Work for the Night is 224

SECOND COMING

Caught Up Together 211
Hallelujah We Shall Rise 118
How Great Thou Art 4
I Want to Be Ready to 138
I'll Fly Away 156
I'll See You in the Rapture 114
Jesus Is Coming Soon 171
O I Want to See Him 117
One Day 246
Redemption Draweth Nigh 77
Some Glad Day 125
That Glad Reunion Day 139
The Old Gospel Ship 214
There's Coming a Day 196
We Will Rise and Shine 206
When It's Time 146

SOLOS, DUETS, MIXED VOICES

All in the Name of Jesus 47
Bring All Your Needs 38
Consider the Lilies 51
Fill My Cup, Lord 13
Follow Me 28
Give Them All to 48
He Looked Beyond my Fault 102
He's As Close As the 49
Holy Spirit, Thou Art 109
How Great Thou Art 4
I Will Glory in the Cross 81
I'm in This Church 210
I'm Standing on the Solid 40
I've Got a Reservation 111
Innocent Blood 98
It Made News in Heaven 44
Learning to Lean 36
Lift Him Up 3
Love Grew Where the Blood 165
Open My Eyes 129
Rise Again 46
Rise and Be Healed 18
Statue of Liberty 24

The Brush 168
The Glove 182
There's a Whole Lot of 137
Through It All 79
What Sins Are You Talkin' 93

SOUL WINNING (See Activity)

SPIRITUALS

Everytime I Feel the Spirit 218
I Feel Like Traveling 152
Just a Closer Walk 208
Kneel at the Cross 209
Neither Do I Condemn Thee 223
No, Not One 74
The Church in the Wildwood 59
The Fire Song 215
The Old-Time Religion 237
We Will Rise and Shine 206
Were You There? 207

SURRENDER (See Consecration)

TESTIMONY

A Beautiful Life 121
Each Step I Take 6
God's Wonderful People 50
He Hideth My Soul 259
He's With Me Always 203
I Learned About Jesus 108
I've Got That Old-time 194
It's Different Now 180
Living By Faith 151
Nailing My Sins to His 83
Somebody Loves Me 190
Statue of Liberty 24
The Brush 168
The Way That He Loves 16
Through It All 79
Way Down Deep in My Soul 161
Where Could I Go? 43
Without a Doubt I'm Saved 193
Yes, I Know 221

YOUTH SONGS

Closer to You 142
Give Them All to Jesus 48
God's Wonderful People 50
Greater Is He That Is 248
Holy Bible, Book Divine 174
I'll Fly Away 156
Jesus Loves Me 213
Lift Him Up 3
Light the Light 135
Onward, Christian Soldiers 254
Surely Goodness and Mercy 89
The Fire Song 215
When the Saints Go 217
Whisper a Prayer 143
Yes, I Know 221

ZEAL

A Beautiful Life 121
Bringing in the Sheaves 31
Closer to You 142
Did You Think to Pray? 181
Higher Ground 220
I Am Bound For the 97
I Am Resolved 10
I Feel Like Traveling 152
I'm In This Church 210
I'm Standing On the Solid 40
Jesus Calls Us 172
Lift Him Up 3
Looking For a City 187
Onward, Christian Soldiers 254
Press Along to Gloryland 120
Rescue the Perishing 261
Sound the Battle Cry 115
We'll Work Till Jesus 205
Will There Be Any Stars? 265
Work for the Night is 224

General Index

A BEAUTIFUL LIFE 121
A country where no twilight 219
A pilgrim was I and a-wand'ring   89
A SONG HOLY ANGELS CANNOT
     SING 91
A wonderful Savior is Jesus, my   259
Alas, and did my Savior bleed . . 23
ALL HAIL THE POWER 76
ALL IN THE NAME OF JESUS 47
ALMOST PERSUADED 86
Altho' I cannot see the way 175
Always, today, tomorrow,
     always 203
AMAZING GRACE 37
Amazing grace shall always
     be my 102
AMERICA 283
AMERICA, THE BEAUTIFUL 284
And He Walks with me and He . 12
And I know, yes I know, Jesus' . 221
And it's a song holy angels 91
Angels never knew the joy that . 91
Angels were rejoicing 44
Are you ready, are you ready? . . 234
Are you tired o' chasin' pretty . . 48
As I journey thru the land 117
As I travel thru this pilgrim 166
ASLEEP IN JESUS 192
AT CALVARY 21
AT THE CROSS 23
AWAY IN A MANGER 276

B

BATTLE HHYMN OF THE REPUBLIC 281
BEAUTIFUL ISLE 19
BLESSED ASSURANCE 27
BLESSED BE THE NAME 160
Blessed Savior, Thou wilt 225
BLEST BE THE TIE THAT BINDS . . 145
Brightly beams our Father's . . . 176
BRING ALL YOUR NEEDS TO
     THE ALTAR 38
BRINGING IN THE SHEAVES 31
By the crowd of worshippers . . . 223

C

Calling today! Calling today! . . . 231
CAUGHT UP TOGETHER 211
'Cause I'll rise again, there's 46
CHRIST AROSE 245
Christ, our Redeemer, died
     on the 63
Christ, the Savior, died for 96
CLOSE TO THEE 195
CLOSER TO YOU 142

COME AND DINE 32
Come, ev'ry soul by sin 84
Come home, come home, it's 116
Come home, come home, ye who . 232
Come to the church in the 59
Come, ye sinners, lost and 221
Coming home, coming home,
     never 233
CONSIDER THE LILIES 51
COUNT YOUR BLESSINGS 20

D

DID YOU THINK TO PRAY? 181
DO YOU KNOW MY JESUS? 61
DOES JESUS CARE? 56
Don't look 'neath the gates 167
Don't you hear the bells now 64
Down at the cross where my . . . 238
Down in my soul, I'll sing 161
DOXOLOGY 186

E

Each day I'll do a golden 121
EACH STEP I TAKE 6
Encamped along the hills of 270
Ere you left your room this 181
EVERYTIME I FEEL THE SPIRIT . . 218
Ev'ry day, ev'ry hour, let me 158

F

FAITH IS THE VICTORY 270
FILL MY CUP, LORD 13
FOLLOW ME 28
FOOTSTEPS OF JESUS 39
For a long time I traveled 136
For all the blessing of the 133
For two thousand years He's . . . 188
From the light of early morning . 203

G

GIVE THEM ALL TO JESUS 48
Glad day, a wonderful day 139
Glory, glory, hallelujah 281
Glory, glory! how the angels 267
GLORY ROAD 177
GLORY TO HIS HIS 238
Go ahead, drive the nails in 46
GOD BE WITH YOU 54
GOD'S WONDERFUL PEOPLE 50
GREATER IS HE THAT IS IN ME . . 248

H

HALLELUJAH FOR THE CROSS . . . 244
Hallelujah! Thine the glory 131

HALLELUJAH, WE SHALL RISE! . . 118
HALLELUJAH, WHAT A SAVIOR! . . 242
HAND IN HAND WITH JESUS 29
HARK! THE HERALD ANGELS
  SING 278
Has fear and doubt came against 18
HAVE THINE OWN WAY, LORD . . . 90
Have you a heart that's weary . . 61
He could have called ten 75
HE HIDETH MY SOUL 259
HE KEEPS ME SINGING 53
He left the splendor of heaven . . 22
HE LOOKED BEYOND MY FAULT . 102
He never said I'd have silver . . . 68
He was wounded for our 252
HE WILL PILOT ME 175
He'll go with me thru the 228
HE'S AS CLOSE AS THE MENTION
  OF HIS NAME 49
HE'S WITH ME ALWAYS 203
HEAR OUR PRAYER, O LORD 103
HEAVEN FOR ME 100
HEAVENLY LOVE 147
HEAVENLY SUNLIGHT 256
Here among the shadows in a . . . 187
Here I stand beside death's 132
Here they bloom but for a 92
HIDE ME, ROCK OF AGES 141
HIDE THOU ME 85
HIDING IN THEE 78
HIGHER GROUND 220
HOLD TO GOD'S UNCHANGING
  HAND 162
HOLY BIBLE, BOOK DIVINE 174
HOLY SPIRIT, THOU ART
  WELCOME 109
HOW BEAUTIFUL HEAVEN MUST
  BE 35
HOW GREAT THOU ART 4
How marvelous! how wonderful! 55
How sweet and happy seem
  those 154

I

I AM BOUND FOR THE PROMISED
  LAND 97
I AM COMING TO THE CROSS 239
I am going to a city where 92
I am looking for the day when . . 216
I AM RESOLVED 10
I am so glad that Jesus loves . . . 105
I am thinking today of that 265
I am trusting, Lord, in thee 239
I am weak but Thou art strong . . 208
I boast not of works nor tell 81
I CAME ON BUSINESS FOR THE
  KING 42
I can hear my Savior calling 247
I can see the lights of home 177
I CAN TELL YOU THE TIME 127

I care not today what the
  morrow 151
I come to the garden alone 12
I FEEL LIKE TRAVELING ON 152
I GAVE MY LIFE FOR THEE 235
I have a feeling in my soul 161
I have found His grace is all 8
I have good news to bring and . . 214
I have heard of a land on the 169
I hear the Savior say, thy 82
I heard an old, old story how . . . 159
I know that I've failed You 142
I LEARNED ABOUT JESUS (IN
  GRANDMA'S ROCKING CHAIR) . . 108
I love the thrill that I feel 50
I must needs go home by the
  way 250
I MUST TELL JESUS 11
I NEED THEE EVERY HOUR 249
I once was lost in sin but Jesus . . 178
I remember the days when I was 93
I remember the time when in . . . 127
I SEE JESUS 106
I SHOULD HAVE BEEN CRUCIFIED 157
I stand amazed in the presence . . 55
I STAND UPON THE ROCK OF AGES 94
I traveled down a lonely road . . . 28
I wandered in the shades of night 62
I want my Lord to be satisifed . . 199
I WANT TO BE READY TO MEET
  HIM 138
I was guilty with nothing to 157
I was sinking deep in sin 9
I was standing on the banks of . . 60
I went to live with Grandma 108
I WILL GLORY IN THE CROSS 81
I will hasten to Him, hasten 10
I will meet you in the
  morning 163, 201
I WILL SING THE WONDROUS
  STORY 255
I WON'T HAVE TO CROSS JORDAN
  ALONE 58
I WOULD NOT BE DENIED 72
I'd like to stay here longer 149
I'LL BE A FRIEND TO JESUS 153
I'LL FLY AWAY 156
I'LL HAVE A NEW LIFE 173
I'LL LIVE IN GLORY 149
I'LL MEET YOU BY THE RIVER . . . 144
I'LL MEET YOU IN THE MORNING . 163
I'LL SEE YOU IN THE RAPTURE . . 114
I'LL TELL THE WORLD 185
I'm a pilgrim and a stranger 217
I'M FREE AGAIN 134
I'm glad Jesus came, glory to . . . 194
I'M GOING HOME 41
I'm in love with my Savior and . . 190
I'm in the way, the bright and . . 170

I'M IN THIS CHURCH 210
I'm learning to lean, learning . . . 36
I'm not even worthy of all of 164
I'm redeemed by love divine . . . 123
I'm pressing on the upward way 220
I'm satisifed with just a 15
I'M STANDING ON THE SOLID
 ROCK 40
I'm trusting to the unseen 197
I've a Friend who's always 228
I've a home prepared where the . 119
I've got a mansion just over 15
I'VE GOT A RESERVATION 111
I'VE GOT THAT OLD-TIME
 RELIGION 194
I've had many tears and 79
I've heard of a land that is 100
I'VE NEVER BEEN THIS
 HOMESICK BEFORE 128
I'VE NEVER LOVED HIM BETTER . 227
I've wandered far away
 from God 233
If I could count the tears that . . 87
IF I COULD HEAR MY MOTHER
 PRAY AGAIN 154
If I leave this world of sorrow . . . 167
If I walk in the pathway of duty . 57
IF THAT ISN'T LOVE 22
IF WE NEVER MEET AGAIN 110
If we never meet again on this . . 114
In New York harbor stands a . . . 24
IN THE GARDEN 12
In the resurrection morning 118
In the sweet by and by we 264
In the very thought of Jesus . . . 49
INNOCENT BLOOD 98
IS MY LORD SATISFIED
 WITH ME? 199
IS THAT THE OLD SHIP OF ZION? . 60
Is the road you're trav'ling 177
IT CAME UPON THE MIDNIGHT
 CLEAR 274
It didn't make the papers in 44
It is joy unspeakable and full . . . 8
IT MADE NEWS IN HEAVEN 44
IT TOOK A MIRACLE 266
It was good for our mothers 237
IT'S DIFFERENT NOW 180

J

JESUS CALLS US 172
Jesus has a table spread where . . 32
JESUS, HAVE MERCY ON ME 164
JESUS (HE IS THE SON OF GOD) . . . 52
JESUS HOLD MY HAND 166
JESUS, I COME 260
JESUS IS CALLING 231
JESUS IS COMING SOON 171
JESUS IS THE SWEETEST NAME
 I KNOW 7

Jesus, Jesus, He's here and 47
Jesus, Jesus, how I trust Him . . . 268
Jesus, Jesus, Jesus, Sweetest . . . 53
Jesus knows all about our 74
JESUS, LOVER OF MY SOUL 226
JESUS LOVES EVEN ME 105
JESUS LOVES ME 213
Jesus, our Lord and Savior, was . 188
JESUS PAID IT ALL 82
JESUS WILL BE WHAT MAKES
 IT HEAVEN FOR ME 100
JESUS WILL OUTSHINE THEM
 ALL 71
JOY TO THE WORLD 273
JOY UNSPEAKABLE 8
JUST A CLOSER WALK 208
JUST A LITTLE TALK WITH JESUS 178
JUST A LITTLE WHILE 183
Just an empty glove lying on . . . 182
JUST AS I AM 45
JUST OVER IN THE GLORY LAND . 119

K

KNEEL AT THE CROSS 209

L

Last night as I was sleeping 204
LEARNING ON THE EVERLASTING
 ARMS 25
LEARNING TO LEAN 36
LET THE LOWER LIGHTS BE
 BURNING 176
Life is like a mountain 225
Life started out like a canvas . . . 168
Life's evening sun is sinking . . . 121
LIFE'S RAILWAY TO HEAVEN 225
LIFT HIM UP 3
LIGHT THE LIGHT 135
Like the woman at the well I 13
Living below in this old sinful . . . 43
LIVING BY FAITH 151
Living He loved me, dying He . . 246
LONELY ROAD UP CALVARY'S
 WAY 17
Long ago, long ago, yes, the 212
LOOD FOR ME AT JESUS' FEET . . . 167
LOOKING FOR A CITY 187
Lord, I saw how You used ole . . . 129
LORD, I'M COMING HOME 233
Lord, let me be the glove You . . . 182
Lord, lift me up and let me 220
Lord, You've tried to use 129
LOVE GREW WHERE THE BLOOD
 FELL 165
LOVE IS WHY 68
LOVE LIFTED ME 9
Low in the grave He lay, Jesus . . 245

M

"Man of Sorrows", what a name 242
MANSION OVER THE HILLTOP 15
Mansions will glisten on the 71
Many times I have wondered . . . 112
MEET ME THERE 73
Mercy there was great and 21
Mine eyes have seen the glory . . 281
MORE ABOUT JESUS 271
MUST JESUS BEAR THE CROSS
  ALONE 101
My country, 'tis of thee 283
MY FAITH LOOKS UP TO THEE . . 107
My Father is omnipotent and . . . 266
My heav'nly home is bright . 41, 152
MY JESUS, I LOVE THEE 122
My latest sun is sinking fast 33
MY SAVIOR'S LOVE 55

N

NAILING MY SINS TO HIS CROSS . 83
NEITHER DO I CONDEMN THEE . . 223
Never grow old, never grow old . 169
NO, NOT ONE 74
NO TEARS IN HEAVEN 251
NOTHING BUT THE BLOOD 240
Now let us have a little talk 178

O

O after while, after while 125
O beautiful for spacious skies . . . 284
O blessed tho't, sweet rest will . . 125
O COME, ALL YE FAITHFUL 279
O COME, ANGEL BAND 33
O ev'ry time I feel the spirit 218
O FOR A THOUSAND TONGUES
  TO SING 95
O for a thousand tongues to sing 161
O how praying rests the weary . . 181
O I WANT TO SEE HIM 117
O I'm gonna take a trip in the 214
O land of rest, for thee I 205
O listen to our wondrous story . . 243
O LITTLE TOWN OF BETHLEHEM . 280
O Lord, my God, when I in   4
O Lord, send the pow'r just 126
O MASTER, LET ME WALK WITH
  THEE 99
O ransomed souls, with joyous . . 120
O Rock of Ages, Hide Thou me . . 85
O safe to the Rock that is 78
O THAT WILL BE GLORY 257
O, the shame of it! my sins 83
O thou blessed Rock of Ages . . . 141
O victory in Jesus, my Savior . . . 159
O WORSHIP THE KING 200
O yes, He cares, I know He 56
O yes, I'll live in glory 149

Oh, how I love Jesus 179
Oh, my loving brother 215
Oh! precious is the flow 240
Oh, say, can you see by the 282
Oh, the judgment day is coming . 215
Oh, what a Savior! Oh 65
Oh, what glory awaits me in 71
Oh, what joy His love affords . . . 50
OLD-TIME POWER 126
On Jordan's stormy banks 97
On the Cross crucified, in great . 252
On the cross of Calvary our 140
On the happy golden shore 73
On the resurrection morning . . . 173
Once a man named Stephen 106
Once from my poor sinsick 29
Once I served the Lord only 193
Once I was lost in sin, I had 180
Once I was straying in sin's 65
Once my soul was astray from . . 66
ONE DAY 246
One glor'ous day Jesus came . . . 199
One night upon the sea, a ship . . 198
ONLY JESUS CAN SATISFY YOUR
  SOUL 104
Only one Man has ever been 98
ONLY TRUST HIM 84
ONWARD, CHRISTIAN SOLDIERS . . 254
OPEN MY EYES 129
Out of my bondage, sorrow and . 260
Over on the bright Elysian shore 144

P

PASS ME NOT 236
Patiently Jesus is calling 229
Praise God, from whom all 186
Praise God, I'm free, I've been . . 134
PRAISE HIM! PRAISE HIM! 269
Praise the Lord, praise the 26
PRECIOUS MEMORIES 150
PRESS ALONG TO GLORYLAND . . . 120

Q

QUEEN OF PARADISE 184

R

REDEEMED 123
REDEMPTION DRAWETH NIGH . . . 77
REJOICE, YE PURE IN HEART 241
RESCUE THE PERISHING 261
REVIVE US AGAIN 131
RING THE BELLS OF HEAVEN 267
RISE AGAIN 46
RISE AND BE HEALED 18
ROCK OF AGES   1
ROOM AT THE CROSS FOR YOU . . 14
Rouse, then, soldiers, rally 115

S

SAFE IN THE ARMS OF JESUS 258
Sailing o'er life's ocean 189
Satan led my soul astray from .. 134
Satan's like a roaring lion 248
SAVIOR, MORE THAN LIFE 158
Savior, Savior, Hear my humble. 236
See my Jesus on the cross 165
See the bright Light shine 128
SEND THE LIGHT 263
SHALL WE GATHER AT THE
    RIVER 5
She's the "Queen of Paradise" .. 184
Showers of blessing, showers ... 253
SHOWING MY APPRECIATION 96
Signs of the times are 77
SILENT NIGHT, HOLY NIGHT 275
Sin stained the cross with 68
Since Jesus came and found me . 227
Soft as the voice of an angel 34
SOFTLY AND TENDERLY 232
SOME GLAD DAY 125
Some glad morning when this ... 156
Some morning you'll find me ... 112
Some people look around and see 135
SOMEBODY LOVES ME 190
Someone here needs help and I .. 42
Sometimes I feel discouraged ... 85
Somewhere, somewhere,
    Beautiful 19
Somewhere the sun is shining ... 19
Soon I'll come to the end of 69
Soon this life will all be over 183
Soon we'll come to the end of ... 110
SORRY, I NEVER KNEW YOU 204
SOUND THE BATTLE CRY 115
Sowing in the morning, sowing . 31
STANDING BY THE RIVER 132
STATUE OF LIBERTY 24
SUNLIGHT 62
SUPPER TIME 116
SURELY GOODNESS AND MERCY .. 89
SWEET BY AND BY 264
SWEET HOUR OF PRAYER 202
Sweet is the song I am singing .. 123
Sweetly, Lord, have we heard ... 39

T

TAKE TIME TO BE HOLY 70
TEARS WILL NEVER STAIN THE
    STREETS 87
TEN THOUSAND ANGELS 75
TEN THOUSAND YEARS......... 69
THANK GOD, I AM FREE 136
That day when they crucified ... 83
THAT GLAD REUNION DAY 139

THE BLOOD THAT STAINED THE OLD
    RUGGED CROSS 140
THE BRUSH 168
The busy streets and sidewalks . 52
THE CARPENTER FROM
    NAZARETH 188
THE CHURCH IN THE WILDWOOD . 59
The cross upon which Jesus 14
The cross, it standeth fast 244
THE EASTERN GATE 201
THE FIRE SONG 215
THE GLORY LAND WAY 170
THE GLOVE 182
THE HEALER 252
The joy I can't explain fills 36
THE LAST MILE OF THE WAY 57
THE MASTER OF THE SEA 198
THE OLD ACCOUNT SETTLED LONG
    AGO 212
THE OLD GOSPEL SHIP 214
THE OLD-TIME RELIGION 237
THE SAVIOR IS WAITING 230
THE STAR-SPANGLED BANNER ... 282
THE TIME IS NOW 229
THE UNSEEN HAND 197
THE WAY OF THE CROSS LEADS
    HOME 250
THE WAY THAT HE LOVES 16
The world will try to satisfy 104
Then sings my soul, my Savior .. 4
There have been names that 7
THERE IS A FOUNTAIN 222
There is a land that I have 111
THERE IS A NAME 179
There is an unseen Hand on me . 197
There is coming a day when no .. 30
THERE SHALL BE SHOWERS OF
    BLESSINGS................. 253
There soon will come a day and . 211
There was a time I know when .. 212
There will be a happy meeting .. 139
There will be those who are 137
There's a call comes ringing ... 263
There's a church in the valley ... 59
THERE'S A GREAT DAY COMING .. 234
There's a land beyond the river . 64
There's a land that is fairer 264
There's a light in the window ... 128
There's a ship lifting anchor ... 184
THERE'S A WHOLE LOT OF PEOPLE
    GOING HOME 137
THERE'S COMING A DAY 196
There's not a friend like 74
There's room at the cross 14
There's within my heart a
    melody 53
THESE ARE THEY 148
They bound the hands of Jesus . 75
They tried my Lord and Master . 153
They were in an upper chamber . 126

This Is Just What Heaven
MEANS TO ME 219
This is my story, this is my 27
Thou, my everlasting portion . . . 195
THROUGH IT ALL 79
Through my disappointments . . 40
THROW OUT THE LIFE-LINE 262
Till we meet, till we meet 54
Time after time He has waited . . 230
Time is filled with swift 162
'TIS SO SWEET TO TRUST IN
JESUS 268
'Tis the old time religion 237
TO GOD BE THE GLORY 26
TOUCHING JESUS 191
TOURING THAT CITY 112
Troublesome times are here 171
TRUST AND OBEY 2
Truth and beauty and happiness 47
'Twas His blood, His precious . . 140

U

Up from the grave He arose 245
Up the Calvary way went my . . . 17
Upon the mountain thro' valley . 218

V

VICTORY IN JESUS 159

W

Walk boldly to stand in His 38
Walking in sunlight, all of 256
WAY DOWN DEEP IN MY SOUL . . 161
We are climbing Jacob's 206
We have a heavenly Father 51
We have heard about His coming 146
We praise Thee, O God, for the . . 131
We read of a place that's 35
We shall rise, hallelujah, we 118
WE THANK THEE, LORD 133
WE WILL RISE AND SHINE 206
WE'LL WORK TILL JESUS COMES . 205
We're gonna be caught up 211
Well, I said I wouldn't tell 130
WERE YOU THERE? 207
WHAT A DAY THAT WILL BE 30
What a fellowship, what a 25
WHAT A FRIEND 88
WHAT A PRECIOUS FRIEND 228
WHAT A SAVIOR 65
What can wash away my sins? . . 240
WHAT DID HE DO? 243
What joy 'twill be when we 219
WHAT SINS ARE YOU TALKIN'
ABOUT? 93
When all my labors and trials . . . 257
WHEN GOD DIPS HIS LOVE IN
MY HEART 130

When He reaches out His hand . 198
When I come to the river at 58
WHEN I SEE THE BLOOD 63
WHEN I SURVEY THE WONDROUS
CROSS 80
When I was but a boy in days of . 116
When I've gone the last mile 57
WHEN IT'S TIME 146
When Jesus came, He was left . . 210
WHEN MY FEET TOUCH THE STREETS
OF GOLD 216
When pangs of death seized on . . 72
When the angry winds are
blowing 94
WHEN THAT OLD SHIP OF ZION SAILS
IN HOME 189
WHEN THE ROLL IS CALLED
UP YONDER 67
WHEN THE SAINTS GO MARCHING
IN 217
WHEN THE SAVIOR REACHED
DOWN FOR ME 66
When the trumpet of the Lord . . 67
WHEN THEY RING THE GOLDEN
BELLS 64
When upon life's billows you . . . 20
When we walk with the Lord . . . 2
When with the Savior we enter . . 155
WHERE COULD I GO? 43
WHERE HE LEADS ME 247
WHERE THE ROSES NEVER FADE . 92
WHERE WE'LL NEVER GROW OLD 169
WHILE SHEPHERDS WATCHED
THEIR FLOCKS 277
While upon the isle of Patmos . . 148
While we pray and while we
plead 124
WHISPER A PRAYER 143
WHISPERING HOPE 34
Who saved us from eternal loss? . 243
WHY NOT NOW? 124
WILL THERE BE ANY STARS? 265
WITHOUT A DOUBT I'M SAVED . . . 193
WONDERFUL GRACE OF JESUS . . . 272
WONDERFUL LOVE 113
WON'T IT BE WONDERFUL
THERE? 155
WORK FOR THE NIGHT IS COMING 224

Y

Years I spent in vanity and 21
Years of time have come and . . . 77
Yes, I feel like traveling 152
YES, I KNOW 221
Yes, I'll sing the wondrous story 255
Yes, Jesus loves me, yes 213
You may have your worldly 138